HOW to Be a DOMinant DiVa

BY Georgia Payne and Julie Taylor

AVALON PRESS

LOS ANGELES

How to Be a Dominant Diva
By Georgia Payne and Julie Taylor

Published by Avalon Press, LLC
3371 Glendale Blvd, Suite 164
Los Angeles, CA 90039
www.dominantdiva.com

DESIGNED BY ANNE MARIE HORNE

PHOTOS BY IAN RATH

Manufactured in Italy

10 9 8 7 6 5 4 3 2 1

Library of Congress
Cataloging-in-Publication data is available

ISBN 0-9769671-0-3

This book is geared toward couples in happy, healthy relationships
who practice safe and consensual sex. Readers who choose to
participate in the sexual games, acts, and techniques found in this
book do so at their own risk. In addition, any product, website, or
service mentioned is merely a suggestion and not an endorsement.

This publication is sold with the understanding that the author and
publisher are not engaged in rendering medical, psychological, or
any other kind of personal or professional services described in this
book. If the reader requires personal or medical advice or other
assistance, a competent professional should be consulted.

The authors, Avalon Press, LLC, and its distributor expressly
disclaim liability or accountability to any person(s) with regard to
any losses or damage caused or alleged to be caused, either directly
or indirectly, by the information contained in this book.

THANKS A MILLION ●

First, we would like to thank **our readers**—all those Dominant Divas out there who know what they want, in and out of the bedroom, and aren't afraid to pursue their passions. You go, Divas!

Our graphic designer, Anne Marie Horne, and production manager, Jennifer Miller: You both possess awe-inspiring talents and expertise. You two are true Dominant Divas. There is no way we could have done this without you! We thank you from the bottom of our hearts for your creativity and enthusiasm. We really appreciate all the late nights that you spent working to make this book so beautiful.

Ian Rath: You are an amazing photographer and friend. We are so excited we found someone who could bring our vision to life!

Keikabou, Jennifer, Isabella, JD, Naomi, Eden, Jay, Michael, and Heidi: We couldn't have chosen more gorgeous and talented models to appear on these pages. You truly got the Diva philosophy, and your fun, anything-goes attitude infused life into the pictures and our book.

Stephanie and Tania: Thank you for giving us the idea for our Doors of Desire format. That lunch where you showed us the snake book was unforgettable. Knowing our book was in your hands put our minds at ease.

Kurt Hassler: Thank you for the inspiration! We will never forget that night at the bar when the idea to write this book struck us like a bolt of lightning.

Elizabeth Whiting and Steve Kleckner: We can't thank you enough for your undying support (and for helping us get in the door)!

David Wilk and Steve Black: We appreciate your taking a chance on us!

Diana, Elizabeth, Christian, Seth, and Jorge: Your hard work and attention to detail were amazing.

Kip: Thanks for always believing in Julie, and for sharing your words of wisdom.

Michael Flattery: Lawyer extraordinaire…thanks for the legal advice!

Our amazing friends, clients, editors, and colleagues: You're too countless to mention by name, but you know who you are!

Freda Taylor: Julie's amazing mom passed away in 1999 at age 52, but she'll never be forgotten. She was truly fabulous and always encouraged Julie to follow her dream of being a writer. What a Diva…

Our supportive families: No matter what, you were always okay with our roles as sexperts and encouraged our offbeat paths in life. For that, we thank you.

Julie's kiddos: A heartfelt hug goes out to Julie's two adorable children, who never fail to make her world more playful and magical.

Our husbands, Greg and Jay: Last but not least, we would like to give a special nod to the awesome men in our lives. You inspired us inside the bedroom and out! Thank you for experimenting with us and never being afraid to indulge our fantasies. And kudos for always embracing and celebrating the Dominant Divas we are.

WHAT'S INSIDE HOW TO BE A DOMINANT DIVA?

69 titillating sex games to excite and inspire you!

JUST OPEN tHE
DOORS OF DESIRE...

Be a Diva

We want to let you in on a little secret: There's nothing better than taking control of your sex life and your man. It's so empowering to know that you're not only in charge of your own O, but you can easily take charge of his, too! Long gone are the days of women just lying there in the missionary position like a dead fish, waiting for the guy to finish. (How depressing!) We're two women who firmly believe sex should be daring and fun. Sure, we're into toys and we totally love our vibrators, but we also believe there's no substitute for the real deal—especially when it both curls your toes and boosts your bond. In our opinion, the sex suffers if you and your partner don't feel free to express your-selves in every way. So that's what we intend to help you do…step by step, game by game, and orgasm by orgasm. Join us on this Dominant Diva journey, and your sex life will never be the same!

WHY US?

Over the years, we realized we were having much better sex than our friends. So many of our gal pals confessed that the passion play of their relationships had

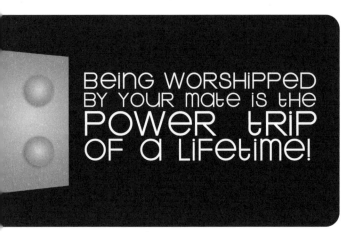

BEING WORSHIPPED BY YOUR MATE IS THE POWER TRIP OF A LIFETIME!

hit intermission...and were starting to ask our advice on how we kept things so hot between the sheets. Once we shared a few tips and tricks, the response was always the same: "Ohmigod, I had the best sex last night!" Soon, more friends…and friends of friends…began to call for nuggets of our wow-oh-wow wisdom.

Something about our sex advice clicked with women. Maybe it was because our experiences comple-mented each other so well. You see, we've been best friends for more than 10 years. When we met, we were both waitresses, but soon we started serv-ing people in other ways. Georgia was the first to take the leap: She became a dominatrix in 1994, and went on to become one of the top dommes in both Manhattan and Los Angeles. Julie wrote her first sex feature for *Cosmopolitan* in 1995 and has been making her living sharing sex advice in magazines ever since.

For the past decade, Georgia has helped thousands of men explore their fantasies and is paid upwards of $300 an hour to do just that. Julie has educated millions of readers on such titillating topics as "Finding His Secret Sex Spots" and "Unleashing Your Inner Sex Kitten." We even did a dominatrix session together once—and held a spanking contest on the guy's ass!

We're best buds who tell each other absolutely everything—including things that would make even the "Sex and the City" girls blush. And every time we'd dish about a new sex technique, fetish, or position, we'd inevitably try it on our husbands and then compare notes. If it earned our seal of approval, we'd tell our girlfriends and spread the love. (We're firm believers in good orgasm karma!) But the more we shared our unique sex advice with others, the more obvious it became that we had stumbled upon an unbeatable erotic equation:

Dominatrix secrets + sex writer wisdom = Hot Dominant Diva sex!

We just knew we were on to something major…and we wanted to share our secrets with the world. Thus, *How to Be a Dominant Diva* was born.

Together, we compiled our 69 favorite sex games so you can get in on the fun, too. These are the best of the best—culled from Georgia's client history, Julie's magazine sex features, and our own erotic experiences. We give you step-by-step instructions, breaking each game into hands-on sections like *Passion Props*, *The Set-Up*, and *Game On!* We also took some super sexy photos to inspire you. Just swing open the Doors of Desire and dive into your next sexual adventure!

In your hot little hands, you now hold the sex secrets of both a leading sex writer and one of America's most successful dominatrixes. What will happen when you incorporate our tell-all tricks into your own sexual repertoire?

You're about to find out, Diva! But first, invest in some fire-retardant sheets, because things are gonna get hot. *Really* hot. And that's a promise!

Love Yourself First

One passion prop you will need in each and every one of our sex games is confidence, Diva. There is nothing more beautiful in the world than a confident woman. From the boardroom to the bedroom, she owns it. She rules and she knows she rules!

But if your own confidence is a little shaky, how do you build it? First, accept yourself for who you are. If you're always thinking, "Damn, I wish my thighs were a little smaller" or "Ugh, my stomach's sticking out—I don't want him to touch me there," you are never going to be able to truly get into or enjoy sex. Do you think guys worry about their love handles or receding hairline when they're doing it? Hell, no! They're focused on getting their freak on, and that's it. And that's the attitude you should have, too.

Look, your guy is already into you, or else he wouldn't be with you. He thinks you're beautiful. So believe it. Embrace it. Work it. You're hot! The more you love and accept your body, the better your sex will be. And having steamy, no-holds-barred sex is what this book is all about! Here are four confidence-boosting tips for the Diva-in-Training:

• When your man says you look amazing or showers you with compliments, take mental notes. Remember all his sweet statements when you're having a bad hair day, PMS-ing, or breaking out your fat jeans.

• Buy at least two outfits that make you feel seriously sexy. Wear them on blah days for an instant pick-me-up.

> **It's all how you look at it...**
>
> **Big butt = Bootylicious**
>
> **Plus-size = Voluptuous**
>
> **Too skinny = Svelte**
>
> **Flabby = Curvy**
>
> **Small boobs = Implant-free!**

• Listen to feel-good music. Pumping up the volume can also pump up your passion, so go ahead—dance around your room naked and shake that groove thang.

• Resist the urge to put yourself down. If you're constantly telling others how frizzy your hair is or how blotchy your skin's been lately, you're not going to feel like the sex goddess you are. Be your own biggest fan!

We love sex—but we both have really busy lives, so we're sometimes just too exhausted or stressed to get it on. Sound familiar? Here's how we help ourselves go from tired to inspired.

• Take time after a busy day to unwind and decompress. Drink a glass of wine, take a hot bath or meditate (even for five minutes).

• Schedule a standing date night with your partner. Make it a top priority!

• Flirt with your man. Tell him how sexy he looks, or playfully squeeze his buns as you walk by.

• Look your best! Sticking to your grooming regimen can pave the way to passion. Georgia gets her hair done every four weeks, and Julie is religious about getting a monthly Brazilian wax. These little indulgences will make you feel sexier, making them well worth the effort and expense.

> **"Sex appeal is fifty percent what you've got and fifty percent what people think you've got."**
> —**Sophia Loren**

• Splurge on some sexy lingerie. A rhinestone-studded thong can go a long way toward psyching you up to get down!

• Book a private date with your vibrator before the lovemaking begins. Play just long enough to get your juices flowing.

• But the best advice we can give you is...READ THIS BOOK! Taking time out to enjoy these sex games together and mix things up in the bedroom will put you in the mood every time!

PRE-PLAY RULES AND REGULATIONS

The 69 sex games found in this book can be extremely liberating—inspiring you and your partner to unleash your deepest fantasies and desires. But they also require an immense amount of trust. To make the most of your experience, we've established guidelines to follow on your path to sexual ecstasy.

1) create some ambiance.
Your surroundings matter when it comes to sex. No one wants to make love on dirty sheets or surrounded by piles of laundry.

2) exercise the power of veto.
We believe most of our games will appeal to you, Diva. (In some of the more outrageous games, we've even offered a "Mild Side" and a "Wild Side" to give you more options.) But if you or your partner just aren't into one of the role-play scenarios, move on to the next! Don't make a big deal about it or shame the other person for not wanting to try. No worries!

3) open your mind.
Communication and acceptance are key to a successful relationship—so never shut your partner down for wanting to try something new or kinky! When he gets turned on, try to be supportive, not judgmental, and encourage him to do the same. Even if you don't want to act something out, you might choose to play out his—or your—out-there fantasy verbally.

> "Handcuff me to the bed. Bree, you are not going to regret taking this journey with me. This is going to infuse our marriage with more passion then you could imagine. You just have to trust me."
> —Rex Van De Camp,
> "Desperate Housewives"

4) play it safe.
Due to the intimate nature of these games and the level of trust required, we don't recommend playing sex games with someone you have just met or are casually dating. And never put your or your partner's health at risk—practice safe sex.

6) Remember: Pain Does Not Always Equal Pleasure.

Sure, some of Georgia's clients are masochists, but most guys aren't. Keep that in mind when playing games that include a punishment/reward system. When you dole out the punishments, don't physically hurt him. The goal is to turn him on, not beat him up!

7) Avoid Verbal Abuse.

Contrary to popular belief, you don't have to yell or get mean when playing power-exchange games. Some of Georgia's clients love being called a "pathetic worm," but the majority of men are not into this. Unless he specifically tells you that he is aroused by verbal abuse, don't go there!

8) Keep It Clean.

We cannot begin to tell you how unsexy it is to have dragon breath or reek of body odor while trying to seduce or be seduced by your mate. Take the time to freshen up before getting it on! And always keep those sex toys clean, too.

9) Establish a Safe Word.

Before you play these games, choose a safe word together. This is a word or phrase such as *mercy, red light,* or *stop* that you've both agreed will halt the game the second it's uttered. Safe words should be accepted and respected for all sex games, no questions asked.

10) Make the Time.

Most of our sex games take little or no prep, but some do. Before you tell yourself you just don't have the time to deal, think about what a healthy sexual relationship with your partner is really worth. When you first hooked up, you probably spent tons of time planning special sexual surprises, right? You'll get out what you put in!

11) Check Your Inhibitions at the Door.

If you encounter a sex game you're intimidated to try, go ahead and push your boundaries. Some of the best sex we've ever had has involved techniques we were initially afraid to experiment with. Be bold. Be daring. Be a Diva!

SPANKING TIPS AND BONDAGE BITS

Once you start swinging open those Doors of Desire, you'll encounter many games that involve spanking or light bondage. But before you play, you need to familiarize yourself with a few safety essentials.

GEORGIA'S SEVEN RULES OF SPANKING:

1) Warm-up is important. Start the spanking session by slightly cupping your hands and lightly hitting each buttock one at a time, always targeting the fleshy, middle part of his butt.

2) A good way to gauge how hard you should spank is to watch your partner's reaction. If he's having a tough time taking it, use a lighter touch. But if he tells you to make it harder, by all means go for it! Your goal is that he enjoy the sensations.

3) Gently rub the skin after every few strokes. Rubbing creates a more sensual vibe, increases blood flow, and allows your partner to take the next stroke with more ease.

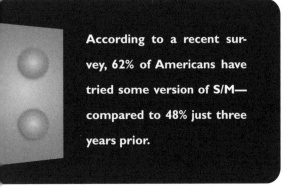

According to a recent survey, 62% of Americans have tried some version of S/M—compared to 48% just three years prior.

4) Lightly scratch the buttocks with your fingernails after you rub them to boost arousal.

5) As you increase your count, add a little sting to your swat! Make sure you up the intensity slowly and always rub his buttocks between smacks. You will start to see a pink, rosy color appear as your strokes get more intense.

6) If his cheeks start taking on color right away, ease off a bit. The coloration of the buttocks is a slow process when done right.

7) Spread his legs apart slightly so that you can gain easy access to his jewels and inner thigh area. Use your free hand to play with him while you spank.

now that you've mastered the art of spanking, it's time to move on to Georgia's basics of bondage:

1) Scarves, neckties, and stockings are fine for tying up your partner. But because they tend to tighten during play, they can cause discomfort or even a pinched nerve. Plus, knots can be difficult to untie. So proceed with caution.

2) When using rope, always stick with thick cotton or nylon. It's best to cut rope into four 15-foot pieces (one for each limb). Immediately secure the ends with electrical tape after cutting the rope to keep them from fraying.

3) Never tie your partner up (or down!) too tightly. Cutting off circulation to the extremities can be dangerous. If your partner is experiencing tingling or numbness in these areas, release him immediately.

4) Never tie a rope around a person's neck under any circumstances. Doing so can be life-threatening.

5) Always keep a pair of scissors nearby. We recommend bandage scissors, as they have a blunt lower blade. That way, you can cut your man out of the restraints without fear of scraping him.

6) Always exercise judgment and common sense when using restraints. Never leave your partner tied up for long periods of time.

7) Check in and communicate during bondage play. Is he all right? Does everything feel okay? You are the one solely responsible for your partner's well-being.

For more tips, visit our website at www.dominantdiva.com.

> "Maybe some women aren't meant to be tamed. Maybe they need to run free until they find someone just as wild to run with."
> —Carrie Bradshaw,
> "Sex and the City"

Before You Play...
Trick Out Your Toy Box!

Most of our sex games do not require any unusual, hard-to-find toys or paraphernalia. However, a few passion props show up in our games again and again, so it will pay to have these on hand. When shopping, remember the four B's!

You are going to need plenty of slippery stuff to help guide—or "glide"—you where you need to be!

What's Hot
- **Water-based lubes (such as Astroglide) are a favorite among Divas! Did we mention they're nonirritating and petroleum free?**
- **Silicone-based lubes are wonderful, and a little goes a long way, baby! And unlike water-based lubes, they're great for water sex.**

What's Not
- **Petroleum- and oil-based lubes. These can stain fabric and destroy latex! Never use with a condom or other latex-based contraceptives.**

1) Blindfolds
Night masks: We love satin or fur ones. So totally decadent!

Scarves: Silk scarves are another excellent (and elegant) way to steal his sight.

2) Bondage
Cuffs: Hand and ankle cuffs are a must for a Diva's toy box! Authentic, double-locked cuffs (like law enforcement officials use) can be purchased in adult stores or online.

Rope: Cotton or nylon rope is readily available at your local hardware store.

3) Beauty
Diva: For that ultimate Dominant Diva look, you must own a black bra, with matching panties, garter, and stockings. And don't forget the stilettos!

Dude: His one wardrobe must-have is a black studded collar—the perfect accessory for your favorite pet!

4) Blastoff!
If you don't already own a vibrator, run, don't walk, to the nearest adult store and indulge, Diva! While you're there, you might want to also buy a vibrating cock ring for your man. This will come in handy sooner than you think....

What do the icons that appear before each of our sex games mean? Use the key below to unlock our Doors of Desire, and then unleash the Diva from within!

HOW MUCH?

Ⓢ	=	FREE
$	=	$1-$30
$$	=	$31-$60
$$$	=	$61-$100+

SPECIAL NOTES

◢	Testing your boundaries
◢◢	Pushing the limits
◢◢◢	Wild and daring
◢◢◢◢	Off-the-charts erotic
✈	Travel involved
☏	Call the babysitter

Now that you know the rules, you're ready to play, Diva! As far as your guy's concerned, the information in this book should be dispensed on a need-to-know basis: Just tell him you bought a hot new sex-game book, and he's gonna get laid!

Then bust open those Doors of Desire. You'll notice some of the doors are marked "Men's Room." That means it's time to hand the book over to your partner. Prepare to be pampered!

CALLING ALL DIVAS!

For even more inspiration, visit our website and Diva blog at www.dominantdiva.com to read blood-pumping bonus content, learn our latest man-handling maneuvers, and meet other daring Divas who are just as fearless as you are!

How often or in what order you play the games is up to you. You call the shots!

GAME ON!

PUT THE PLAY IN ROLE-PLAY

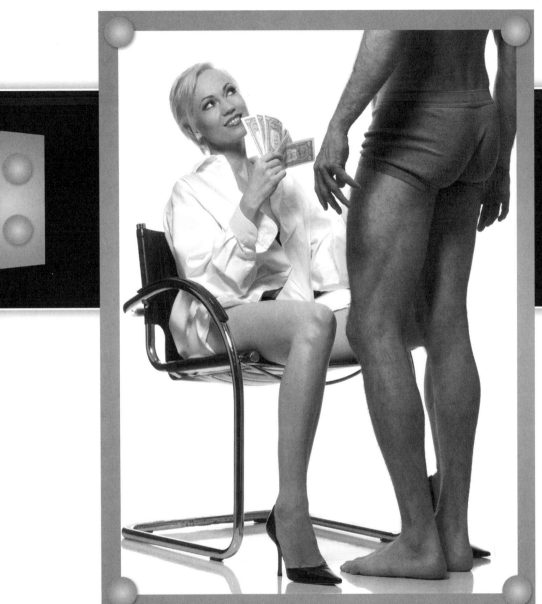

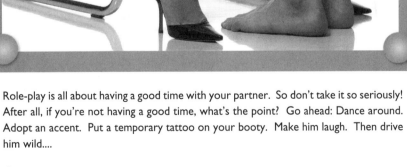

Role-play is all about having a good time with your partner. So don't take it so seriously! After all, if you're not having a good time, what's the point? Go ahead: Dance around. Adopt an accent. Put a temporary tattoo on your booty. Make him laugh. Then drive him wild....

THe Set-uP

A hot man, a chair, sexy music, and attitude are all you need to fulfill this torrid fantasy. Queue up four classic heavy metal stripper anthems, then tell your man he's going to do something special for you tonight. You're going to sit in a chair in the middle of the room, and when the music starts rocking, so will he. His mission? To do everything in his power to make you hot! If he's shy about dancing in front of you, no worries. Assure him that you're not judging his moves—you just want him to do whatever it takes to make you drip with desire!

Let him know he's allowed to touch and caress you, but it's against the rules for you to touch him. (He doesn't want you to be thrown out by security, does he?) Tell him you have 20 crisp singles, and he has to earn every last dollar in order to win this game. But there's a three-song limit. If he's victorious, he'll get to escort you to the back room for some one-on-one action. If he loses, he gets nothing. Those are the rules, and you plan to follow them to the letter.

Have a seat and tell him to hit "play" when he's ready. If he wants to slip into something more stripper-friendly, let him do so while you enjoy a glass of wine and get ready for the show.

Game On!

When the action begins, tell him he has a one-song warm-up period. This is prime time for you to gear up, too, Diva. After all, you have a role to play here as well. You are the patron and he is a hot piece of meat! Your eyes alone should communicate that you want to eat him alive. When the first official song kicks in, talk dirty! Tell him how hot he is and how you want him to work hard for the money. Invite him to come over to your lap and feel how wet he's making you! Let him know that he's your pretty little boy toy who exists solely to please!

What if he starts slacking? Or stops turning you on? Demand that he work harder. Suggest a body part he needs to focus on, or a particular dance move you'd like to see. Wave the dollar bills in his face as incentive to pull out all the stops.

When you're nice and hot, tell him to flash his manhood to give you a taste of what you're missing. Of course, you want to see the grand prize before giving all of your money away. Time for him to show some skin!

Will he win that last single before the third song is through? If so, join him in the back room for your private lap dance—in the buff, of course. If he's a good boy, you might even treat him to a dance of his own!

DIRtY
DanceR

Tonight, you're a bachelorette, and he's a hot male stripper who practically oozes sexuality. It's your last night of freedom, and you plan to make the most of it! But there's something different about this male stripper. He knows just how to make you hot, and his sole goal in life is to get you into the back room. To do so, he has to earn every last dollar you have. With each dollar bill you tuck into his thong, he'll have to work harder and harder for the next. Does he have what it takes to win the ultimate reward?

Passion Props

Four Rockin' Songs
20 One-Dollar Bills
One Chair

DIRtY Dancer

Stock up on those dollar bills, Diva—it's time for your guy to shake his moneymaker. And who knows? If the night goes well, you might just take this male stripper to the back room to get a sneak peek at what's filling out that thong!

LAP OF LUXURY

When you tell your man you have a special night planned, he'll never guess what kind of erotic mischief you've got in mind! But this time he has no say in the matter....

THE SET-UP

First, e-mail him the following mysterious message at work:

Surprise date night tomorrow! I've planned something very special. Be ready at 7 p.m.

He'd never dream in a million years that a strip joint is what you have in mind—even though that's exactly where you intend to take him! But don't let him in on your secret just yet. You don't want to ruin his surprise!

Throw him off the trail by taking him to dinner first. Tease and taunt him through the meal, dropping little hints about your next destination. Make him order something hearty—because he is definitely going to need his strength to get through this evening!

After dinner, drive him to your strip club of choice. He'll likely be in shock as you pull into the parking lot. Have you made a wrong turn? But when he sees the smile on your face and that glimmer in your eye, Diva, he'll instantly know that you have something naughty up your sleeve—and that he's one hell of a lucky guy!

In your sexiest voice, tell him: "Surprise! I'm about to buy you the best lap dance you've ever had. But I get to choose who dances for you. You have no say in the matter! And I intend to watch your lap dance up close and personal—like my own private porno movie!" Whoa.

Game on!

Enter the strip club and choose a seat by the stage. Let your guy know that you're imposing a gag order—he isn't allowed to say a word. He can only shake his head yes or no. As the strippers gyrate in front of you, ask your guy specific questions: "Do you like her ass?" "Do her boobs turn you on?" Playfully graze your fingers over his crotch to up his excitement factor.

Once you've grilled him about the dancers, relish in the knowledge that you and you alone have the final decision. Call over the stripper who most turns you on and say, "I would like to buy my guy a special dance!"

Negotiate the deal as your guy sits by, speechless. You have the power! Hand her the cash, and promise a generous tip if she makes your guy hard. *Really* hard. Remind your guy that if he utters one word, this dance is over! Then sit back and enjoy the show. Watch your man wiggle and squirm as he gets a hot lap dance with an even hotter Diva like you by his side! (Talk about a double whammy!) Whisper naughty things in his ear. Tell the stripper all the things he can't: how hot she looks and how erotic her dance moves are. When you're his mouthpiece, it will drive him absolutely wild!

Once the show is over and you've tipped your dancer, tell your man he's allowed to talk now. We bet the first thing out of his mouth will be that you're the sexiest Diva in the world!

LAP OF LUXURY

We've all heard enough bachelor party war stories to know that guys looooove strip clubs. That's a given. But why should those Y-chromosome types have all the fun? It's time to turn the tables, Diva, and join in the action! The twist? You're in total control here—and your man must follow your every whim. If he so much as utters a syllable, this party's over....

Passion Props

Dinner Reservations
Strip Club Destination
Cash for Lap Dancer

unmask
tHe Romance

Everyone's sex life hits a rut now and then, so it's up to you to mix things up. When you send him on sexy errands and give him sensual surprises, it's a surefire way to rejuvenate the romance and reignite the passion. A good Diva always keeps her man guessing, "What will she think of next?"

THE Set-UP

Call your man and tell him that you would like him to pick up a special package for you after work. If he starts to ask questions, just tell him this is something that his Diva would like him to do. That little hint will let him know that this is a special errand indeed, and he'd best follow orders! Go ahead and give him the address, but not the name of the store. Don't even hint that he will be visiting your local porn shop. Let him make that discovery all on his own! Tell him to call you from his cell for further instructions when he reaches his destination.

As your guy approaches the address you've given him, his mind will race. Why are you sending him to a porn shop? Have you been shopping for him there? Don't worry: Your man's overwhelming curiosity will overpower any and all fear or embarrassment! When he calls you for his marching orders, tell him to pick up the package left in his name from the store clerk. Warn him that he is forbidden to look inside. His mission is simply to pick it up and bring it straight home to you. No peeking!

Once your errand boy makes the pickup, the drive home to his Diva will indeed be a long one! It will be all he can do to stop himself from ripping open that package at the next stoplight....

Game on!

Your man is home at last. Now tell him he just has to endure a bit more mental torture before showtime. Make him prepare the bedroom just the way you like it, with soft music playing in the background and lit candles. If he doesn't set the stage perfectly, make him do it again! The wait will only add to his building anticipation.

Once the room meets your satisfaction, it's time to blindfold your guy. Ask him to unwrap his present, then make him guess what it is. If he guesses wrong, "punish" him by giving him love bites along his neck or spanking him lightly, then give him another chance. Once he answers correctly, remove the blindfold and let him see his prize. Enjoy your toy together all night long!

errand BOY

Try springing some new sex toys on your guy, and odds are he'll spring right back. That's why you're going to leave work a little early today and head directly to your nearest adult store. It's time to add a new toy to your sexual bag of tricks! This toy could range from mild to wild depending on what turns you on. Will it be a vibrator, paddle, or butt plug? Once you've made your decision, simply purchase your toy of choice and leave it with the clerk for later pickup. Be sure the bag is stapled together tightly so your guy won't be able to sneak a peek!

passion props

One Sex Toy • Candles
A Favorite CD • Blindfold

erRand BOY

You've got an important errand for your man to run after work. There's definitely something in it for him, too…as long as he can follow his Diva's explicit instructions!

◢◢◢$

TReasure HUnt

We've all heard that the brain is the biggest sex organ. Well, today, you're going to screw with his mind in a major way! And it will all start with a little treasure hunt....

⌐$$$[

THE SET-UP

Give your man a note with an address, the time, and a name on it. Tell him that he'd better not arrive a minute late or there will be serious consequences! What he doesn't know is that the address is a nail spa, and the person mentioned on the note is the manicurist you met earlier. Let's call her Roxanne. The note should say:

Please go to 555 Helms St. at 2 p.m. Ask for Roxanne!

Adrenaline will pulse through his body as he makes his way to his destination. Where is he going? Who is Roxanne? Is she a massage therapist?…a stripper?…a hooker?

GAME ON!

As he approaches the nail salon, he still won't know quite what's happening. After all, most guys don't get manicures! But that's all about to change. When he enters and asks for Roxanne, she'll tell him that his Diva has treated him to a full manicure. As she pampers his hands, he'll feel like royalty. Once the manicure is done, Roxanne will tell him that the bill and tip have been taken care of—but she has a special surprise for him. She'll hand him an envelope with "Please read this silently to yourself in front of Roxanne" written on the front.

He'll surely blush as he reads the note inside:

I hope you enjoyed your manicure today. I wanted your nails to be nice and clean for when you come home and finger me tonight. I can't wait to feel those buffed nails deep inside of me!

The note will also direct him to another address. He's to be there at 4 p.m. and ask for Jenni. This time, the address is the local lingerie boutique, and Jenni is the saleswoman you spoke to earlier. She hands your man the $40 gift certificate, along with a note saying:

Please use this gift certificate to purchase me something totally naughty. Then bring it to the following address and ask the bartender for Kelly.

Just picture it: Your man is standing in a lingerie store with a stranger named Jenni, and he's been charged with picking you out something sinful! That's hot.

Time for the last stop: a cozy bar or restaurant. He goes up to the bar and asks for "Kelly." You have already arrived and told the bartender to direct anyone looking for Kelly to you. Be sure to wear a hat and keep your back to the door. That will allow you to conceal your identity until the last second! As your guy approaches, his head will spin as he wonders just who this Kelly is and exactly where this game is going. At the last possible moment, twirl around and reveal your glorious Diva self. As you kiss his newly manicured hands, say, "Congratulations! You just completed my treasure hunt. Now let's check out that sexy lingerie you bought me!"

He'll be so blown away by all the effort you've gone to…we bet he's never felt so special!

TREASURE HUNT

Divas love being on their guys' minds—and today, you're going to dominate his every thought! All it takes is a little planning. Before you play this game, go to your nearest nail salon and then prepay for a manicure for your man. Give the manicurist a sealed envelope to present to him when the manicure is over. Tip big! She deserves it. Next, go to the lingerie store and purchase a gift certificate in your guy's name. Leave another envelope for your sweetie. And make sure this one is sealed with a kiss....

PASSION PROPS

One Nail Appointment
One $40 Gift Certificate
One Hat

PUSH HIS
BOUNDARIES

Being a Dominant Diva doesn't mean you're a whip-wielding drill sergeant who barks orders in the bedroom. On the contrary, a Dominant Diva is a woman who knows what she wants and how to get it in a way that's sexy, not scary. She oozes confidence from every pore and never fails to rock his world.

THE SET-UP

Before the massage starts, set up his parlor. You'll need candles, soft music, body oils, and a beach towel on the bed for you to lie on. Hide a vibrator under the pillow—he'll definitely need that later!

Game on!

When you enter the room, disrobe and lie face down on the towel. Your masseur proceeds to spread oil all over your body, then begins working on your back, neck and shoulder blades. Doesn't that feel good? Don't you wish you were treated to this sort of luxury every night?

Once he's done with your back, turn over so he can massage the front of your body as well. Ask him if he minds massaging your breasts, as they're sore from a previous workout. In no time, he'll plunge right in and give them the attention they deserve. His touch is so exquisite, you can see why he is always booked up—and you tell him so. You feel so comfortable with him that you decide to ask him to do something about that tension between your legs....

"How about a happy ending?" you inquire. "I'd love you to get me off with a vibrator." He'll likely be shocked—and delighted!

Hand him the vibe and let him do what he does best. Close your eyes and enjoy the sensations until you reach full orgasm.

He's worked up by now...so tell him you'd like some of that "special lotion" he's so famous for. You'd like him to touch himself and come on your freshly massaged stomach. If he asks you to rub him, too, tell him that you don't do that to strangers. After all, you're the client here! That means you're in control of this situation, and what you say goes. The fact that you won't touch him will bring him even closer to the brink. Be sure to look into your masseur's eyes while he pleasures himself. And when he explodes, tell him how much you love his manly massage cream. After all, he made it himself!

HAPPY endings

Tell your guy that you'd like him to give you a full-body massage before bed. (Assure him that you'll reciprocate when you get to the "Sex Spa" game—he gets a massage in that one.) All he needs to know is that he's a professional masseur tonight! But don't let on that this is anything but a normal massage. That way, he'll be even more surprised when the evening takes a decidedly erotic turn....

Passion Props

Candles • Soft Music
Oil • Towel • Vibrator

HAPPY endings

Imagine you're meeting your man for the first time. He's super hot, and you bet he'd be amazing in bed! Go ahead: Proposition him. Treating him like a sex object can be a big turn-on for you both!

👠 $

FIRe
and ICe

Teasing him with different hot and cold sensations is a classic move you can easily incorporate into your lust life. Not only will you heighten his skin sensitivity, you'll turbocharge both your libidos!

THE SET-UP

First, assemble your props next to the bed and light the candle before calling him into the room. Tell him that he's going to be your boy toy, then slowly strip him down. Command him to lie down on the bed face up.

Game on!

Now, get on top of him like you're going to ride him. Take his jaw into your hand and lean in as if you're going to place a hot kiss right on his juicy lips. Just as you are about to kiss him, push his face away and lightly nibble his neck. Whisper that you plan to have a little fun before you take him. Then blindfold him with one of your scarves. Kiss every inch of his face before you take his wrists and bind them to the bedpost with the other two scarves.

Slowly work your way down to his shaft. Play with it. Then begin to give him a BJ. Once he is fully erect, put a small piece of ice in your mouth and treat him to some freezing fellatio. This will electrify his nerve endings and energize him all over.

Hold a fresh cube in your mouth and draw an icy line along his entire body. Spend some time tracing circles around his erect nipples—they can be just as receptive to pleasure as yours are!

Now that he's nice and cool, it's time to take him to the boiling point. Remove the lit candle out from its holder and raise it high above your sex slave's chest. It's important to keep the candle as high above your partner as possible. The closer the candle is to the skin, the more heat he will feel, since wax cools as it falls. Concentrate on the areas that you've already traced with ice. The droplets of candle wax will feel fab on his cold nipples. Always avoid the face and neck, which are ultrasensitive. (If you happen to get wax in his hair, simply apply baby oil or peanut butter afterward and it should slide right off.)

Once he's about to combust, chill him out again. Run the ice along his testicles and penis, circling the head with the frosty cube. Tell him he has to trust his Diva while you "heat him up down there." This will scare and excite him at the same time, as he'll think that you are going to put candle wax on his prize! Remind him that he's tied down and that he agreed to be your little toy for the evening. In order to get sex, he needs to lay back and take it!

Put your candle near his penis (but not too close!) to let him feel the heat. Since he can't see what you are doing, adrenaline will course through his body in fear and anticipation. Tell him to trust you—then slowly drip the wax on his inner thighs instead.

Reward him by stroking him and telling him what a good boy he is. Since he was so trusting, it's time for his reward: a night of lovemaking with his Dominant Diva.

FIRE
and ice

By experimenting with different temperatures between the sheets, you'll heighten his skin sensitivity, increase blood flow, and pump up arousal. (All good!) But this game takes major confidence—so if you've never played with wax, you might want to practice first on your own thighs or tummy. Always use an unscented white paraffin candle. (These are the emergency candles found in most grocery stores.) Colored, scented, or beeswax candles generate much more heat, so they're a definite no-no.

passion props

Three Scarves • One Unscented White Paraffin Candle Candle Holder • Bowl of Ice

WHEN PUSH
comes to shove...

Roughing him up in the bedroom communicates primal, need-you-now desire and sparks unbridled passion. When you shove him, spank him, or pull his hair, a surge of pleasure-inducing endorphins flood his system, which will turn him on even more. So show him who's boss, Diva!

GODDESS GAME 1: WILD SIDE

THE SET-UP

While he's in the shower, lay out a pair of your sexiest panties on the bed (or a bigger pair that you've purchased beforehand). Make sure they're soft and silky. Men certainly don't want to be controlled by a pair of granny panties!

Many guys at some point in their lives have tried on or worn women's panties. And even if they've never actually done it, many guys have thought about it. In fact, more than three-quarters of Georgia's clients pay her big money to dress them in women's underwear! And these are high-powered, *straight* CEOs and businessmen. Why the fascination? Women's undergarments are much softer and silkier than men's briefs, so they feel good. Period. Many guys are just too afraid that women will think they're gay if they admitted this desire, so they keep it to themselves. But if you ask him to do it for you, he won't have to deal with any insecurity or fear. He's doing it to please you!

Game On!

When he gets out of the shower, tell him it would please you if he wore your panties all day long underneath his clothes. Be authoritative and let him know that if he truly wants to satisfy you, he will abide by your wishes! Explain that every time he takes a step, he'll feel the silky smoothness of those panties, which is his cue to think about what you're going to do to him tonight. His reward? If he wears the panties all day, he'll get to make love to you all night! Once he gets home, strip those panties off and take him on the ride of his life. He'll be raring to go after this full day of groin attention!

GODDESS GAME 2: MILD SIDE

THE SET-UP

If you're pretty sure your guy wouldn't be into wearing panties, lay a shoelace or long ribbon on the bed instead. Or try a sex toy designed to hold his penis in place, such as a lasso or cock ring.

Game On!

When he gets out of the shower, tell him you're going to bind his penis so he can feel your presence all day long! If you're using a ribbon or shoelace, wrap it around the base of his penis and testicles, then tie a bow (just not too tight). Or snap the cock ring in place. Tell him that this should serve as a reminder that you are in control of his penis—and that today it's your property! If he's a good boy and wears it all day, you'll remove it and play with your "package" when he gets home!

The best thing about this game is that your guy will think about you nonstop all day! That restricting squeeze play under his boxers will spark thoughts of all the naughty ways you'll use and abuse him later. When he gets home, do just that!

UNDER PANTS

Start the day off right and sexually excite your man before he goes to work. This game has two variations. One involves him wearing women's panties—something many of Georgia's clients are very into. But if your guy is anything like Julie's husband, who wouldn't try that for a million dollars, we've explained how to play this game another way.

PASSION PROPS

Women's Underwear (his size)
Shoelace, Ribbon or
Cock Ring (choose one)

UNDER PANTS

Have you heard the news? There's a party in his pants...and you're most definitely invited!

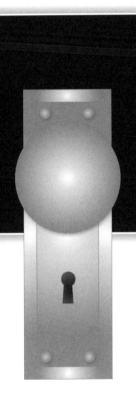

PARKING LOT
PASSION

Those boys' nights out can get pretty rowdy! But they've never gotten crazier than this....

THE SET-UP

First, get him to plan a boys' night out at his favorite bar. If he hasn't gone out in a while, why not suggest that he hang out with his friends this week? You could even throw him off by telling him you're having a girls' night out on Friday, so he should plan something with the guys as well.

That night after he heads off, put on your sexiest dress, your highest heels, and your deepest red lipstick. Once you're properly dolled up, give him a call to check in. The goal of this call is to confirm his location. If he decided to blow off his favorite watering hole and go to Hooter's instead, you need to know that—because that's where you're going, too! (Only he doesn't know that....)

GAME ON!

Once you're in the parking lot of his destination, give him another call. He'll probably be surprised that you're calling a second time, so make it snappy: "I need you to go out to the parking lot for a minute. I sent over a surprise for you—but you must go alone!" Curiosity killed the cat, and it will surely set a trap for your man. He won't be able to resist investigating what his Diva is up to this time!

As he steps outside, he'll find you in your car with the motor running, looking hot as hell. Tell him to get in. Then say, "I know you're having a good time with your friends, but I just need five minutes with you to make your night even better."

Now, drive to the farthest corner of the parking lot and pounce! Depending on how secluded it is, you can make out with your man, give him a hand-job, or even go the blowjob route. But remember: You've only got five minutes!

Once the time is up, send him back to his buddies. And be sure to mention that you'll be waiting in bed for him naked when he comes home!

When the guys see that smile on your man's face, they'll no doubt wonder what he's been up to. He'll either have a mind-blowing story to share or a great secret to keep, depending on how discreet he is. But boy, is it tempting to tell them how hot his Diva is! The guys would be soooo jealous....

PARKING LOT
PASSION

You've always been the kind of gal who's cool with her guy having a boys' night out. You're not really the jealous type, Diva—because you're 100% confident your guy couldn't do any better than you. But haven't you ever been the slightest bit tempted to crash his little party—just once? Now's the time to make that happen!

Passion Props

Cell Phone
Car

TRADE IN YOUR
FLANNELS FOR FISHNETS

In the life of a Dominant Diva, wardrobe is important. No, we're not suggesting you get tricked out in fishnets and garters every night. But every once in a while, it's fun to get all glammed up for an evening of lovemaking. When you look sexy, you feel sexy!

THE SET-UP

You've been slaving away in the lunchroom (translation: kitchen) all day when you see your guy sneaking a pudding cup from behind the counter. Who does this punk think he is?

"I saw that!" you reprimand, prying the cup from his clenched fist and stashing it in your pocket. "Uh, but..." he stammers, at a loss for words. You're used to this reaction from the guys in school. While most lunch ladies are mousy and matronly, you're voluptuous and hot. "Come with me," you say, dragging him into the storeroom (translation: bedroom). On your way, grab another pudding cup—you'll need it later.

You're determined to teach him a lesson. "How old are you anyway?" you ask, slamming the storeroom door shut. "Eighteen," he answers. "Good," you say. "At least you're legal." You unbutton your uniform a few buttons at a time: "Does this make you hot?" you ask seductively. "Uh...yeah...of course," he says, as the bulge in his jeans grows even bigger and bigger.

"Good," you whisper, rubbing his growing erection through the straining denim. "Because I'm going to teach you a lesson."

GAME ON!

Undo his jeans and release his manhood. Give him a few strokes just to tease him. Put the pudding cup on the end of his love rod, and smear it up and down his taut skin. Stare deep in his eyes as you command, "I want you to touch yourself, then lick your fingers clean."

As he does this, tell him what a bad boy he's been...and that this is how naughty boys get treated. Emphasize how ashamed he should be that he resorted to stealing. Tell him how much you hate thieves. Though luckily for him, you love chocolate....

Get down on your knees and ask Mr. Delinquent if he's learned his lesson. If he hasn't, make him touch himself even more. If he has, tell him that's good—because all this reprimanding is making you hungry, and it's time for your dessert.

Then slowly lick the pudding off his manhood until he passes the point of no return. (He'll be so turned on, this shouldn't take long!)

Now, take the second pudding cup out of your pocket and tell him that since he likes pudding so much, you want him to smear it all over your hottest spots, then lick it off. Remind him that he can't stop until you hit your O! But he should hurry: His break's almost over, so he better eat all his lunch!

sweet TOOTH

Georgia's clients just love role-play scenarios where she's caught them doing something naughty!

Here, you're the hot lunch lady all the guys fantasize about. And you just caught your man stealing a pudding cup from behind the counter. He's in big trouble now! After the tongue lashing he's about to receive, he'll never steal sweet treats again.

passion props

Two Pudding Cups

SWEET
TOOTH

There he goes, acting up in the
lunchroom again. He's been a bad,
bad boy. Now it's time for him to
be punished!

↙↗ $

CROSS-DRESS to IMPRESS

Imagine you're a man trapped in a woman's body and there's a hot vixen you're just dying to screw....

THE SET-UP

Tonight, you're going to raid his closet. Anything's fair game: His crisp fresh-from-the-cleaners shirt, his favorite T-shirt, even his beloved jeans…belted and rolled up, of course. Wearing his boxers or briefs is a definite turn-on, too. And be sure to grab one of his ties—you'll need it later!

Slick your hair back or pull it into a ponytail. Complete the look with smoky eyeshadow and liner along with bright red lipstick.

Game on!

When you enter the bedroom, be authoritative. Tell him what you want and how you want it. Secure his wrists with his necktie. Let him take a peek at those boxers of his.

You really want to play up your dominant role here. Tell him that you're going to have your way with him tonight. You always thought he was a little slut! Many of Georgia's clients love pretending they're damsels in distress. If your guy is into this, go with it. Otherwise, just imply that he's your nasty little play toy.

Open his shirt (or rip it off if it's an old one) and feel up his chest. Pay extra attention to his nipples. Tell him how much you love his "tits"!

Next, stick your hand down his pants. Say how nice and wet he feels down there. It's obvious how much he wants you—so there's no use in denying it. Grind against his pelvis and tell him how hard he makes you!

When you're both worked up to a frenzy, pull his manhood out of his pants and take his boxers off. Tell him how good and tight his pussy feels. If he's into it, ask him how much he likes your hard dick. Since you're both playing different gender roles here, his masculinity shouldn't be threatened in any way.

Plus, haven't you always wondered how an orgasm feels for a guy? If all goes according to plan, you'll soon be able to find out for yourself! Schwing!

CROSS-DRESS
TO IMPRESS

Gender-bending is something that Georgia and her clients experiment with a lot. Guys love taking on a more feminine role while she assumes a more masculine one. It all starts with the look.

Put on his white dress shirt with his boxers underneath. Giving his masculine wardrobe a feminine twist is a great way to pump up all your power plays...and the passion! But your attitude is just as important. Take control and be forceful. Go ahead—embrace your Inner Dude!

Passion Props

His Clothes
One Necktie

can you keep a secret?

A Diva knows that sharing sexual secrets with her man is a sure way to fuel the passion. Cop a feel under the table at dinner or whisper naughty things to him in the middle of a crowded room, then wait for fireworks!

THE Set-UP

A few days beforehand, tell him to leave Saturday open, because he's spending the day with you. On Friday night, leave a note on the dresser that says: *Tomorrow, we are going shopping together. This is no ordinary trip, and I won't take no for an answer. Please meet me in the bedroom at 11 a.m. ready to go. Await further instructions.*

Saturday morning, spend a little extra time primping. Your look is important here—but you're going to be doing a lot of walking, so dress accordingly. You can't go wrong with a flowy dress or a silk top with straight trousers, as long as your outfit is paired with cute but comfy shoes.

Game On!

Good news, Diva: We've given you two options here. Read them over, then decide which one's right for you. (Can't decide? You can always do both—one today, one next Saturday!)

GODDESS GAME 1: WILD SIDE

First, tell your guy that your mission is to train him to love shopping, and you've got something that will help you do just that. Command him to drop those drawers while you secure the vibrating cock ring to his manhood. Give him a sample buzz just for kicks. Say, "When I see you looking bored today, you're going to get a love buzz from me! I'm in charge—and I have no problem using the remote control as often as I wish!" Just zip up his pants, drop the remote in your bag, and you're good to go.

Once you arrive at the mall, head straight to your favorite store and ask him to pick out something sexy for you. The moment he starts slacking, buzz him back to attention! But don't do it when there are lots of people around. Use discretion. Really make him squirm, as you are relentless in your pursuit for male perfection. (Must. Like. Shopping. Dammit!) Next, visit his favorite store, then give him another jolt for fun. Sexually torture and tease him. After the third store, hit the food court—and buzz him again. Be ruthless! Because when you get home, he's going to take out all that pent-up sexual tension on you and only you....

GODDESS GAME 2: MILD SIDE

If cock rings aren't his thing, don't despair: You can still train your guy to love shopping. Drag him to the mall. First, hit a department store and ask him to select five pairs of panties for you. (Hot!) Then pick out some jeans for him in the men's department and join him in the dressing room for a quick make-out session. (If women aren't allowed, don't worry—just tell him that you're going to wait outside for him to model his clothes so you can see how his package looks in those pants!) Have lunch at Hooter's or a testosterone-filled sports bar to refuel. On the way home, stop by a sex shop for a hot porno to watch later. He'll go shopping with his Diva anytime!

FOREPLAY
STORE PLAY

It's a fact of life: Most women love to shop, and most men pretty much hate it. The majority of red-blooded American males would rather have their eyes plucked out than follow their Diva around a shopping mall. However, this shopping spree is going to be different...*way* different! Your man just needs the right incentive to join you, that's all!

Ready to teach your man to looooove shopping, Diva? In our experience, there is no better way to train a man than by using his "other head."

PASSION PROPS

Remote-Controlled
Vibrating Cock Ring

FOREPLAY
STORE PLAY

Think about that buzz you get when you find that killer skirt or the perfect pair of shoes. On this shopping extravaganza, you'll give him a different kind of buzz!

⌃⌃⌃⌃$(

DRIVE-THRU
DESIRE

Ready to tap into your exhibitionist side? Making him give you an O in public is bold, but no one needs to know your secret....

⚡⚡⚡⚡$$$(

THE set-up

First, purchase a pair of remote-controlled vibrating panties at your local adult store or online. Two of the more popular options include the tiger panty and the butterfly. (Both are available at www.goodvibes.com.)

Tell your man you're taking him out to dinner somewhere fancy. Get all dolled up. Take the keys and declare that you're driving, but keep your destination a secret. He'll no doubt be curious—and will feel positively puzzled when he sees you approach a fast food restaurant.

Surely you didn't ask him to get all dressed up for burgers and fries, did you?

Not exactly.

Game On!

As you pull into the parking lot, hand him the remote control to the vibrating panties you have on. His mission: To make you hit your O before your order is ready. If he succeeds, you'll take him for drinks and dessert at the fanciest restaurant in town as a reward.

Encourage him to send you a love buzz as you place your order. Trying to speak—much less form a sentence—while your panties are vibrating is difficult, for sure, but the good news is that it feels fantastic.

We can just hear you now: "Aah…I'll take a burger…and, oh oh…fries…and an…ooooooh-migaaaaawd, iced tea…."

Your guy will be hard in two seconds knowing how wet he's making you, so be sure to tell him how good all this buzzing feels. As you drive from the order board to the window, encourage your sweetie to caress your breasts or rub between your legs. If you're feeling extra frisky (and brave), tell the drive-thru attendant that your man is making you feel reeeeeeeally good right now. (Or command your guy to make that confession!)

If you do not have an orgasm at the first drive-thru, don't despair—just hit another…and another…until you pass the point of no return. Each new drive-thru is just another scene for some hot foreplay!

Even if the clerk doesn't hear the buzz, focus on the fact that you're about to have an orgasm in front of a total stranger. What a turn-on! As the drive-thru guy hands over your change and then your food, look him straight in the eye as you climax. Now give your man a nice, long, juicy kiss. Toast to your sexual good fortune at that fancy-schmancy restaurant you promised him you'd visit—then top the evening off with some hot, raunchy sex when you get home.

DRIVE-THRU DESIRE

Okay—the last time you were at a drive-thru, there were probably French fries involved, right? Well, tonight, the only thing French you'll be sampling at your nearest fast food joint is French kissing!

PASSION PROPS

Remote-Controlled
Vibrating Panties • Car

OUT OF SIGHT, not out of mind'

A Dominant Diva isn't dominant 24/7. (How boring would that be?) So switch things up: Let him take the reins every now and then and treat you like the Goddess you are! Remember: Being in control is hot, but being controlling is not. Besides, sometimes the most fearless thing you can do is to let go....

THE SET-UP

Put the dildo in very warm (but not hot) water 10 minutes before playtime to heat the center. Lay all your new toys on the bed, then place a bottle of baby oil and a bowl of ice cubes on your nightstand. Light a few candles, then call her into the bedroom.

GAME ON!

Ready to tickle her fancy? Begin the game by blindfolding your Diva, then laying her down on the bed. Lightly bind her hands with scarves or rope. Spread her legs apart so that you gain easy access to all her hottest spots. Start by rubbing a small amount of oil on her arms, legs, and torso. Rub and massage her entire body, paying special attention to her breasts and genitals.

Once you have gotten her nice and warmed up, start by tracing the vibrator all over her breasts, abdomen, arms, and legs. Alternate the buzz of the vibrator with little kisses and love bites. Trace a finger from her inner thigh down to her toes. Once her nerves are tingling with excitement, tease her clitoris with the vibe. Alternate between buzzing her clit and pulsing the vibrator in and out, in and out.

Now it's time for some dildo action. She's already lubed from the baby oil, so the dildo should slip right in. It's so deliciously warm, she's likely to combust! (And when you ask her how she likes that big dildo inside her, she'll get even hotter!)

After a few minutes of dildo delight, replace it with an ice cube for maximum chills and thrills. Tease her clit with the vibrator as you slide the ice cube inside her. Then place another ice cube in her mouth, and tell her to suck on it like she's going to suck you later!

Time to get busy! As you make love, tell her you have one last surprise. Now pull out the love beads. (These are small jelly-like beads that are inserted inside the anus to increase pleasure.) Lube is your friend here, so be generous with it. Gently insert the beads inside your Diva. Make sweet, slow love to her as she enjoys the flood of sensations. Once you see the signs that she's getting close to orgasm, prepare to pull the love beads out at the moment of climax. This will intensify her O!

You've made your Diva feel so good, there's no doubt that she'll return the favor. Prepare to be devoured!

TOY
BOX

Just because she's all grown up doesn't mean that your Diva has outgrown her toys. Treat her to some erotic goodies from your local sex shop or online. If you don't already have the following items in your sexual treasure chest, here's what you'll need: love beads, a vibrator, and a dildo (preferably glass). Glass dildos are more expensive, but they retain heat longer and feel warm to the touch.

Diva Disclaimer: This game will be hot for you, too—but try not to come before she does. The passion will be more intense if you hold out as long as you can!

Passion Props

Vibrator • Scarves or Rope
Dildo (preferably glass)
Love Beads • Blindfold • Oil
Scarves • Candles • Ice Cubes

TOY BOX

men's
ROOM

Tell your Diva you just got some
spanking new toys, and we guaran-
tee she'll come over to play....

⌐⌐$$

naKeD SUSHI

She'll be delighted when she hears you're cooking dinner—and even happier when she finds out that you'll be eating off her.

⌐⌐⌐⌐$

THE SET-UP

First, decide on your menu and do your shopping. Think finger foods here. We recommend going with a fruit or sushi motif. If you choose the classic sushi route, take-out is way easier than do-it-yourself. Save yourself the trouble and pick up some rolls from your sushi bar ahead of time.

Ask your Diva to take a nice long bath as you prepare the cuisine. Let her know that she should not put on any perfume or other scents, as it will interfere with the smell and taste of the food. And when she's done, she should come to the table naked. (This will give her something to think about while she's soaking in the tub!) Once you have the kitchen all to yourself, go ahead and prepare your feast, then put a long white tablecloth on the table. Put some soothing background music on. Now, pour a glass of wine and wait for your centerpiece!

Once your Diva arrives in her birthday suit, help her lie down on the table, face up. She might feel a little nervous or self-conscious about being on display like this, so ease her mind by assuring her how beautiful she looks. Encourage her to take a deep breath and close her eyes. She needs to trust you. Explain that she is going to be your motionless centerpiece tonight, and you're going to eat your meal off her supple skin.

Game on!

Slowly and deliberately decorate your Diva's body with all the scrumptious delicacies you've gathered. Tell her to savor the feeling and texture of the foods being artfully arranged on her soft flesh. Just imagine placing sushi rolls over her nipples and pouring soy sauce in her belly button! If you are serving fruit instead of sushi, place the largest and most succulent piece of fruit inside her love lips. Pour chocolate syrup all around her clitoris.

Once the food is laid out to your satisfaction, it's time to enjoy. Bon appetit! Without using silverware, lean in to nibble the food from her nipples. Tell her how amazing everything tastes. Drip the juices all over her pores. Surely she's built up an appetite watching you devour this in-the-buff buffet, so serve both yourself and your lover.

As the feast draws to a close, it's time to lick your "plate" clean. It just so happens that this plate has beautiful breasts and a hot mound for you to devour! Lick as much of her sweet, salty skin as you can before making love to her right there on the table. You've never been so hungry for each other…and it's time to satisfy your every urge!

naked SUSHI

Level with us, guys: You like good food and you love good women! Why not mix the two together for an evening of complete hedonism? Tonight, you are going to lay your naked Diva out on the dinner table and dine off of her sweet body. The art of Naked Sushi—where sushi feasts are served off a woman's bare skin—started in Japan and has spread to restaurants in Los Angeles, New York, and the like. And now, this hot trend is coming straight to your dining room!

Passion Props

Fruit • Chocolates
Sushi • Soy Sauce

make HIS HarD DRIVe
even HarDer!

Surfing the web together for online porn can actually boost your bond. In fact, recent studies have shown that many couples experience a "Viagra effect" after looking at erotic material online with their partner. What a great reason to log on...then get off...together!

THE Set-UP

First, pick your chatroom of choice. Since chatrooms come and go, check out our website at www.dominantdiva.com for the most up-to-date list of our favorites. A few of the best chatrooms can be found at www.adultfriendfinder.com and www.alt.com. Adult Friend Finder offers a wide variety of couples chatrooms including the "Couples Couch" (our favorite!), whereas the edgier Alt.com rooms—such as "Couples Cage" and "Cyber Sex"—cater more to the dominance and submission crowd. Before logging on, dim the lights in your home office to set the stage.

Game on!

Enter the chatroom and start a game of Dare or Double Dare. Announce that you and your man are currently taking requests on what you should do to each other next. Tell the group that you're both naked, then casually mention that you have some rope, whipped cream, and lube ready to go. (This icebreaker will give the group a springboard to jump into your naughty little game!) As you fulfill the chatroom participants' requests, report your reactions back to the group. For example, if another Dominant Diva tells you to tie your guy up, let her know how much he's moaning as you tighten the rope around his wrists or how hard he's getting as you do so.

If you're not comfortable sharing your cybersex adventures with a big group, consider joining another couple in a private chatroom for some two-on-two action.

For more of a Diva twist, check out a chatroom that caters to the female dominant. Once you enter the room, plot with another femme fatale on the fate of each of your submissive significant others! Afterward, you could always reverse the roles so that your man schemes with a male dominant to decide your destiny!

Chatrooms can be ultrafun and safe, but you still need to take precautions. Anonymity is key here. Never give your personal information or identifying details to anyone, even if he or she seems to be the coolest person in the world. First off, you have no idea what sort of person (or psychopath) you're dealing with here. Plus, meeting a couple from a chatroom face-to-face is entirely different from chatting with them online. Think of these people as mere props for your sexcapades (cool!), not real-life humans you'd actually bring into your bedroom (uncool!).

Continue your naughty chatroom games until you've both gotten off—or log off before you reach orgasm, and take your sexcapades into the bedroom.

HOT CHAT

You don't have to be a sex addict or a total pervert to enjoy online eroticism. Visiting chatrooms with your mate allows you to be as adventurous and explicit as you dare, while remaining completely anonymous. If you haven't tried this yet, now's your chance!

Passion Props

Computer • Whipped Cream
Lube • Rope

HOT CHAT

Visiting a chatroom together can be an easy but exciting way to broaden your sexual horizons. Enter if you dare....

GIRLS GONE
WIReD

Sure, he loves checking out Internet porn. But he's never looked at it quite like this!

THe Set-UP

Once you've learned your way around a website or two, start investigating what your guy would be into. Casually ask him to what kind of fantasy would really get him off. Is he into girl-on-girl, women dominating men, or even group sex? Get as many specifics as you can. If he's too shy to talk about his fantasies, reveal one of your own to get him going.

After you've discovered what your dude likes best, plug the relevant keywords into your favorite search engine to see what's out there. Pull up five to ten photos, erotic stories, or any other sites of interest.

Game on!

Ask your man to take a seat in front of the computer, then tell him you have something to show him. Tell him you've been thinking a lot about his secret fantasy, and you think he's been a bad, bad boy for withholding it from you for so long. He's in for some serious punishment! Use your best authoritative but sultry tone.

Pull up the first photo and tell him you want to see if it gets him rock hard. Now unzip his pants and uncage his monster. Stroke it, play with it, and get it right where you want it. We would be willing to bet that there will be no resistance.

Once he's fully erect, click on the erotic story. Tell him he must read the story aloud in its entirety while you give him a BJ. As the lady of the house, you have no choice but to milk your naughty man for having so much sexual tension! He is not allowed to climax before the story is finished, nor is he allowed to stop reading.

If he gets through the story, come up for air and click on the most graphic site you've selected. Command him to look at the photos and to explain his fantasy in more detail. Tell him that he can be as nasty as he wants! After a few minutes, give him permission to come at any time since he's controlled himself this long. What a good boy he is!

After he ejaculates, it's your turn to have some fun. Trade places with him and type in a few erotic keywords of your own—whatever your heart desires. Then surf away while he licks you down there and makes you feel mmm-mmm good!

GODDeSS TiP: ONLY SUrF FOr POrn ON YOUr HOMe COMPUTer—never at WOrk. POrn iS FAB, BUt it'S nOt WOrtH GettinG FireD Over!

GIRLS GONE WIRED

Have you noticed how the media has recently embraced porn, elevating it from deviant to desirable? Suddenly, a girl who knows her way around an adult site is beyond cool. So start surfing! Then get your guy in on the act, too....

Passion Props

Computer

LEARN HOW to PUSH HIS BUTTONS

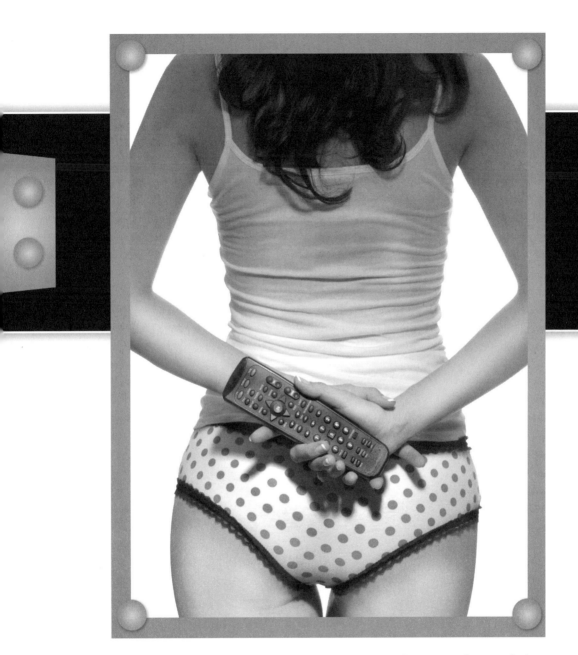

Make it your business to know exactly what gets him hot. Discuss your fantasies. Push each other's sexual boundaries. Experiment with different techniques. Then take lots of mental notes. The more you learn, the hotter it can get!

THE SET-UP

Tonight, you have a surprise for your man, so he isn't allowed to come home until 8 p.m. Make sure you're home by 7 so you have time to set the stage. Earlier in the day, stop by your local sex shop to pick up a porno. (For a list of our favorites, go to www.dominantdiva.com.)

Soak in a hot bath until your skin is silky smooth. After your bath, slip into a pair of your sexiest fuck-me pumps. That concludes your wardrobe for the evening! Light candles around the house to set the mood. Next, place the vibrator, collar and leash within arms' length on the couch in front of the TV. Finally, wrap your scarf around the chair, then place the chair next to the couch.

At 7:55, plop down on the sofa, and turn on the porno and your vibrator at the same time. Get yourself wet before he comes home. Better yet, let him discover you pleasuring yourself!

Game On!

When he walks in and discovers your dirty deeds (and your dirty movie), he'll be intrigued. Leave the porno playing while you command him to take all of his clothes off. Say you have a present for him. Secure the collar and leash around his neck and whisper that he is not allowed to speak or touch himself unless he has your permission. Order him to sit in the chair and be a good boy. Warn him that if he disobeys you, you will take the scarf and tie his hands behind his back.

Now, walk over to him and tell him to spread his legs. You want to see that nice hard rod of his! Stroke it and play with it to your heart's content. Place your vibe under the tip of his penis and watch it grow as he admires your body. You want him to be as turned on as you are. Once he is erect, return to your seat and your movie.

Play with yourself, using the vibrator, and let your fingers slip in and out of your lips. Spread your legs so that he can see what he isn't getting right now. Really let yourself go! We dare you to work yourself into a frenzy in front of your man. Teach him a few new tricks about your wants and needs. Now get up. Take hold of the leash and place your high heel on his chest while you enjoy the buzz of the vibrator on your clit! Stare at him as you get wetter and wetter. You have him right where you want him—obedient and horny as hell!

Do you think you've tortured him enough? Yank him off the chair by his leash and guide his face in between your legs. His manhood should be throbbing right now, but that's too bad! You need attention first. Tell him he's your love servant and that he needs to go down on you now. He's not allowed to stop until you are satisfied! Once you are pleased with his performance, let him know he will be rewarded at a later time. He is not allowed to pleasure himself or make love to you tonight. Your pleasure's all that matters this evening...so he can go straight to bed. He's dismissed.

If he's a good boy and follows orders, wake him up with an erotic early-morning BJ. Don't stop until you send his morning missile into orbit!

BLOCKBUSTER NIGHT

Does he like to watch? Most guys do, especially when it comes to porn. After all, guys are visual—but so are you, Diva! And there's nothing that gets your juices flowing more than watching an adult movie with your man. Sure, the '70s porno music can be a little cheesy, and the actors aren't always exactly sex gods, but watching an X-rated movie is still hot. It's so…bad girl. And tonight you're going to be really, really bad!

Passion Props

One Adult Film • Vibrator
Collar • Leash • High Heels
Scarf • Chair • Candles

BLOCKBUSTER
nIGHT

Tell your guy that you want to stay home tonight and watch a movie. Once he finds out what *kind* of movie, the evening will get way more interesting!

⌐⌐⌐$

sex
scandal

You've just discovered a sex video starring your man. Somebody's got some explaining to do....

⌐⌐⌐⌐$

THe set-uP

After the cameras are in place and the stage is set, it's time to decide on a script. Take a more submissive role in this movie, Diva—the more submissive, the better. (Your ulterior motive will become crystal clear later....)

As soon as you can say "Lights, Camera, Action," it's time to capture your illicit activities on video! Once you have immortalized yourselves on film, the real fun begins....

Game on!

The next day, you are no longer that sexual submissive he made the movie with last night. Instead, you have transformed into a very powerful woman who knows something naughty about him. Leave a note in his briefcase that looks something like this:

I know what you did last night with that submissive slut and I have it all on tape! What would your significant other think of this? I would be willing to bet that she wouldn't be too happy. I am going to make you pay for those indiscretions. Meet me in your bedroom tonight for your punishment. I'll teach you not to treat women like sex objects!

All day long at work, he'll wonder what he's in for!

When he comes home, make him strip down completely. As he is disrobing, explain that you're going to make him watch the video you "found" while you take him in the same way that he took that "slut." Tell him that if he does a good job in sexually submitting to you, you'll destroy the video so that no one gets hurt. If he resists, that means he hasn't truly learned his place. In that case, warn him that you just might keep the video in a secret place so you can blackmail him with it again in the future!

Hit "play" on last night's video. Now, turn the tables and do him like he did the "girl" on the tape. When he gets nasty in the movie, use that as a cue to get nasty with him. (If he was on top, you get on top—and so forth.) Really turn the tables and give him a taste of his own medicine. Use his body for your pleasure!

Once you're done, go ahead and destroy the evidence. Don't worry: You can always make another tape tomorrow night!

GODDess TiP: IF YOU're not uP For makinG Your own sex viDeo, sKiP THe set-uP anD suBstitute tHe Homemade sex taPe in Game on! For a store-BouGHt 'amateur-style' Porn. PretenD tHat Your man is tHe star oF tHe viDeo anD tHat You've DiscovereD His Dirty little secret!

sex
scandal

Pam Anderson. Fred Durst. Paris Hilton. It seems like every other week, a new celebrity sex tape surfaces! Making a racy movie together is not only fun, it can bring you closer together. Are you ready for your close-up? In the very near future, you and your guy are going to film an X-rated flick of your own, and then make sure it lands in the "wrong hands." Will the tape be used against your man? You bet! But that's the best part....

passion props

Video Camera
Videotape

Put Him in a REAL BIND

Handcuffing your guy is a great way to gain control. By taking away the use of his hands, you're putting yourself in the power position. After two simple clicks, you're the one doing all the touching and rubbing, and he's completely at your mercy. If you handcuff him to the bedpost or a chair, even better.... Since he's completely immobile, you can do anything and everything you want!

THE SET-UP

Assemble the passion props on your nightstand. Lower the lights and put some soul music on.

GAME ON!

When you're ready, call him into the boudoir. Command him to stand up straight with his arms at his sides. Tape the plastic wrap to his abs, then encase his upper torso—from biceps to waist. Wrap him more loosely than you'd initially think you'd need to—otherwise, cramps can set in or his breathing can be compromised.

Since you can't wrap his legs while he's standing, help your mummy up onto the bed. Tell him to lift his legs onto the mattress and bend his knees so that you can wrap him from mid-thigh to ankle. By now, he should be completely cocooned. The only parts of his body that should be exposed are his head, neck, shoulders, feet, and groin. He sure looks helpless...just like you like 'em. What to do, what to do?

Start by playing with all of the exposed parts of his body. Kiss his lips and shoulders, then nibble on his neck. Take as long as you want. He's certainly in no position to protest! (If he doth protest too much, you can always tape his mouth shut. Just make sure his nose is uncovered so he can breathe properly!)

Focus your attention down south. Give him a little BJ action, then jump on top of him for a pony ride. Tell him you're a black widow and he's caught in your web. Let him struggle all he wants—he's not getting out! The goal of this game is to please yourself at his expense. Just use him sexually and treat him like a piece of meat! He does look like a piece of meat, doesn't he? All wrapped up in that plastic—all that's missing is the little white foam carton!

Once you've both experienced awe-inspiring orgasms, carefully cut the plastic off his body and free your butterfly boy from his cocoon.

GODDESS TIP: MAKE HIM DRINK A BIG GLASS OF WATER
BEFORE THE GAME BEGINS TO PREVENT DEHYDRATION—AND NEVER
TRY MUMMIFICATION OUTDOORS IN HIGH TEMPERATURES.

BOUND
to PLEASE

You'll notice that many of the toys and techniques we recommend re-surface repeatedly in our games. Blindfolds are a classic, since taking away his eyesight always gives the Dominant Diva the upper hand. Handcuffs, scarves, and rope are also prized props because physical restraint forces the submissive to physically hand over control.

But we like to throw you a curve-ball now and then, and this game's a prime example of something a little off the grid. Ready to take restraint and bondage to a whole new level?

PASSION PROPS

Blindfold
Two Boxes of Plastic Wrap
Scissors • Duct Tape

BOUND to PLEASE

Wrap him up like a present and then check out that package! Talk about plastic fantastic....

$

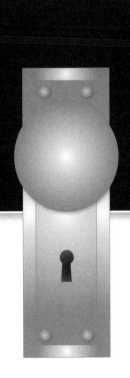

CAUGHT
AND CUFFED

Tonight, you have him right where you want him. It's time to lock him up and throw away the key!

♪♪♪$$

THE SET-UP

First thing in the morning, fill your ice tray with water. Then place both ankle cuff and handcuff keys in the water and freeze to make key cubes!

Let your man know that he will be your plaything tonight and that you have a nice little game in store for him later. That way, he can think about it all day!

Game on!

After dinner, take him back to the bedroom and have him lie facedown on the bed, naked. Handcuff his wrists behind his back then interlace the ankle cuffs through the handcuffs and fasten. This is what Georgia calls "a hogtie in cuffs," and this is the bondage position her clients request most. Not only is your guy now completely cuffed—he can't even walk! Let him stew there for a moment while you go to the kitchen to put your key cubes in a bowl.

Once you re-enter the bedroom, show him the bowl and explain that he'll be imprisoned until the ice melts and he can access the keys to the cuffs. He'll then have to release himself without your help. Set the timer for one hour. If he gets out in an hour or less, you'll perform any sex act he wishes. If he can't break free, then he'll be expected to perform any sex act you wish.

For the next hour, you'll have the house to yourself while he struggles and strains against the bonds. Sip a warm cup of tea or soak in a long hot bath. Indulge, Diva! You have the power, and your sex prisoner is at your disposal. Every ten minutes or so, check in to tease and torture him. Stroke his dick or lick his nipples. Tell him to dry hump the bed. Pet his head and tell him what a good little inmate he is.

Once the hour is up, it's love slave time. Is he fulfilling your wishes, or are you fulfilling his? Doesn't really matter in the end. In this situation, you both win!

cauGHt
anD cuFFeD

Have you ever wanted some time alone to do your own thing or longed for a little peace and quiet? This game will take a bit of prep in the morning, but come nightfall, you will be free to kick back and relax while your man is caught and cuffed!

Passion Props

Ankle Cuffs and Handcuffs
Empty Ice Tray • Timer

PREPARE to BE
STRIP SEARCHED

Intimidation can be highly erotic, especially when it comes to sex and role-playing. If you were being arrested in real life, you'd probably feel like you were living a nightmare, but getting "frisked" by your lover can feel more like a dream come true—especially if you're both convincing in your roles. When you play the part of a cop or another power player, *own* it.

THE SET-UP

First thing in the morning, tell your partner he should expect to be used and abused at some point in the next 24 hours. You may use him in any manner you like at any time or in any place of your choosing. He must submit to your wishes, and he's not allowed to ask questions.

The rest of the day, do not mention this request again. He'll be dying to know what's up—and may even wonder if you have forgotten about it all together. Let him suffer! You'll totally catch him off guard when you attack him after hours.

Before you turn in for the night, make sure your props are in place. Under your pillow, place a pair of handcuffs, a butter knife and three pieces of rope. But don't let him peek!

Before he changes into his pajamas, request that he put on the new pair that you have bought especially for the occasion. These new PJs should be cheap and disposable since you will be cutting and ripping them off him later—but don't let him in on the secret just yet. As for your attire, think easy on, easy off. You're going to be taking off your clothes in the heat of passion, so make sure your PJs don't have too many buttons or hooks.

Game on!

When you're ready to strike, slowly get on top of him and cover his mouth with your hand. To really catch him off guard, wait until he dozes off before attacking him. Tell him in no uncertain terms that if he makes a move, you will off him. Take your hand away from his mouth and grab the handcuffs and rope from underneath your pillow. Handcuff him and shift the cuffs over his head. Using the rope, fasten the cuffs to the bedpost so he can't escape, no matter how hard he tries. Tie each of his ankles to the posts at the foot of the bed so that he cannot kick. (Don't have bedposts? Tie the rope to the legs of the bed frame instead.) While you are tying him up, tell him how good-looking he is, and how you might have to have a little piece of meat before you rob the place. Remember: It is important to use key words and phrases like *rape, use, meat,* and *you know you want it!* If he starts responding, go with it! Take out the butter knife and stroke the dull edge menacingly. Tell him that you want to see his dick and use his hot body. Rip his clothes off while you threaten to rape him. If he isn't completely hard yet, stroke him until he is at full attention. Rub the dull edge of the knife up against his manhood, which is a teasingly threatening move that never fails. Kiss and lightly slap him as you prepare to ride him "against his will"—*yeah, right!*

As you take him, pull his hair and ask him if he likes it. Say that you know he likes it because he is so turned on. If he starts moaning, cover his mouth with your hand while you ride him and whisper that no one can hear. Tell him that he better not make you use your knife! His mind will spin until he is ready to explode.

USED AND ABUSED

At some point, almost every man has fantasized about being forced to have sex or being "taken" by a beautiful woman. There's a steamy scene in Francis Ford Coppola's 1992 film *Dracula* where a group of gorgeous vampirettes take Keanu Reeves' body and blood—and he definitely doesn't put up a fight. Your guy won't either! You just have to set the stage.

passion props

**Blindfold • Three Pieces of Rope
Cheap Men's Pajamas • Handcuffs
Butter Knife • Scarf or Gag**

USED AND ABUSED

Tonight, you're going to take him
against his will. But deep down,
you know he wants it....

👠👠👠 $ $

UNDER SIEGE

He's a hard-core criminal. You're the cop who's about to bring him to his knees. Literally!

THE set-up

Set a single chair in the middle of the room. A bright light overhead will set the tone—but if you don't have one, use a halogen lamp or flashlight that you can shine in his face. The name of the game is intimidation. You want to look like a cop, but this doesn't mean you have to spend hundreds on an official uniform. Cheapie costumes are available around Halloween, or staples from your own wardrobe could always work, too. A white button-down shirt, tan or black pants, and a belt scream, "Don't mess with me!" High heels will amplify your imposing image. If you have longer hair, pull it back—or slick back shorter 'dos for a stern but sexy style. Wear heavy makeup to up the sexy factor.

Before you interrogate him, say what a scumbag you think he is—then strip him down naked. Tell him you might even have to do a cavity search. That way, he'll feel extra vulnerable during the role-play.

Game on!

Sit him in the chair and bind his hands and feet with handcuffs or rope, whichever you are more comfortable with. Blindfold him and step out of the room. Let him ponder his predicament for a few minutes before returning. Once you walk back in, explain that you are the officer in charge and that you will be asking him a series of questions. Whisper in his ear that you are well aware that he knows these answers, and if he spews any lies, he'll be severely punished. If he acts appropriately during the interrogation, he will be rewarded. As you tell him this, place your heel on his crotch and apply just enough pressure to get his attention!

Now, the questioning begins. The fun part of this game is that you get to decide which answers are right and which answers are wrong. When he gets a question wrong, punish him. When he gives you the right answer, give him a reward. Be creative! To spark your imagination, here are some examples of rewards and punishments that are guaranteed to please—and tease.

PUNISHMENTS
- Pinch his nipples with your fingers
- Pull his hair back
- Lightly spank his penis
- Slap his inner thighs with a small ruler

REWARDS
- Stroke your fingernails up and down his shaft
- Place a vibe on his erection for 30 seconds
- Put whipped cream on his balls and lick it off
- Kiss him, but don't let him kiss back

Have a laundry list of questions ready so you can repeat the punishment-and-reward cycle until you are satisfied. And speaking of satisfied, once you have reached the end of the interrogation, tell him the time has come for you to dispose of him. Slowly take your clothes off in front of your criminal as he watches you intently. Tie a scarf or a gag around his mouth, so he won't scream while you *try him out*. With his hands and feet still bound, ride him and pleasure yourself until you are ready to put him back in his cell. Now that's what we call *jailbait!*

UNDER SIEGE

Tonight, he's going to be grilled! All he needs to know: You're the officer, he's the prisoner. And now it's your mission to make him spill his guts!

PASSION PROPS

Single Chair
Halogen Lamp or Flashlight
Police Costume (optional)

He PaMPeRS HiS DiVa
FROM HeaD tO TOe...

You don't have to be a foot fetishist to enjoy the benefits of a good foot massage. A recent study found that a foot massage can actually be linked to sexual arousal. That's because the part of the brain that perceives sensations in the feet is right beside the part that perceives sensations in the clitoral and penile region. Howdy, neighbor!

THE SET-UP

Attach a small note to a collar that says "See me" and leave it on his pillow. When your man approaches you, command him to gather all the passion props and bring everything to the bedroom. Make him light a candle and place it on the nightstand. He should then disrobe and wait for you on his knees, naked.

When he is ready and anxiously waiting, go into the bedroom and slip into something more silky and slinky. Let him watch!

Game On!

Lie down on the bed and tell him that he will be attending to your tired feet this evening. His sole goal (no pun intended) is to make your feet happy. Place the collar around his neck and make him reply: "Yes, Goddess."

First, tell him to soak the washcloth in the warm water and bathe your feet. When he has cleaned them to your satisfaction, make him dry them off completely. Now you would like him to massage your feet with his bare hands. (No lotions or oils yet!) Let him know if he is massaging them too softly or too hard. He needs to be trained to serve you the way that you like! If he is neglecting a certain area, then let him know that, too. Don't be shy.

When both feet feel nice and relaxed, instruct him to cover your tootsies with little pecks. There are 36,000 nerve endings in your feet, and you want him to stimulate every one of them! He must massage and kiss your feet at the same time.

Next, ask him to lick and suck your freshly bathed toes. Some women can even achieve orgasm through this act alone! Are you one of those women? Why not find out for yourself?

Once he's kissed your feet long enough, it's time for him to moisturize his Diva. Tell him to rub the baby oil or lotion all over your feet and legs. If he's served you well, you just might let him massage other areas....

But, no matter what happens next, make sure he keeps that collar on. It's a physical reminder that he is your slave and you are his Mistress...at least for tonight!

PLAYING FOOTSIES

High heels sure look good, but they can really do a number on your sweet feet! Wouldn't it be nice if your man pampered your tired tootsies? Don't wait for him to think of it on his own…drop a hint that he just can't miss!

Passion Props

A Large Bowl Filled with Warm
Soapy Water • Washcloth
Collar • Towel • Candles
Lotion or Baby Oil

PLAYING
FOOTSIES

Would you like your man to wait on you hand and foot? You're about to get half your wish....

Geisha
GIRL

Break out your kimono. Tonight, you're a sexual servant with a few naughty needs of her own.

◢◢◢$$

THE SET-UP

The first thing you'll need to do is groom yourself immaculately. This has always been an extremely important ritual in the life of a geisha—so take your time. Soak in a hot bath scented with jasmine or lavender. Pay special attention to your makeup. Powder that's a shade lighter than your skin and red lipstick will do the trick. Next, pull your hair up away from your neck in a bun or an updo.

In terms of wardrobe, a kimono would be amazing, but a long dress will work, too. Satin sandals or slippers are the footwear of choice. Think Japanese!

When your Samurai gets home, serve him hot tea or warm sake to put him in the right frame of mind. Traditional Japanese music such as Gagaku or Koto will help set the mood. (These types of CDs can be ordered from www.amazon.com.)

Tell him you're a geisha girl who lives to please only him. He is your life. Start by being very passive. Rub his feet. Massage his temples. Avoid eye contact, and speak in soft tones. Call him "sir" or "master." (He'll temporarily wonder if you've undergone a personality transplant... but don't worry, this is all part of the role-play.)

Now, hand-feed him sushi or anything appropriately Japanese, such as tempura or sashimi. Tell him you've got a confession to make: Even though you love catering to his every whim, you've got a few needs of your own. And while you know you're risking public persecution by confessing this, you'd like nothing more than to turn the tables for one hour. For the next 60 minutes, you humbly request that he meet your every need. After the hour passes, you will go back to being his submissive geisha. The memories of this hour of pleasure will sustain you for the rest of your life.

Game on!

Of course, he'll say yes. The minute he does, lead him into the bedroom and set your alarm for exactly one hour later. Now unleash all that pent-up sexual energy and frustration on him. You're like a caged animal who's just been set free! Attack him. Devour him. Talk dirty. Demand he perform lewd acts on you that are illegal in 13 states. Try multiple positions. 69 him. Make love like a porn star!

When the alarm goes off, both of you should make it your business to give each other earth-shattering orgasms (if you haven't already). Then thank your "master" for allowing you this hour of sexual freedom. It's been a night you'll never, ever forget. And neither will he!

geisha GIRL

What man hasn't dreamed of being with a geisha girl? The thought of a woman who lives solely to serve his every need is so hot. (And the fact that she wears that sexy kimono doesn't hurt either!)

A little-known fact about the geisha is that she typically enjoyed freedoms and power other Japanese women didn't. In that sense, she was a Diva.

But tonight, you're going to give the geisha image an Extreme Diva Makeover—and your guy won't know what hit him!

Passion Props

Red Lipstick • Light Powder
Tea • Satin Slippers • Dress
Kimono (optional) • Sushi
Gagaku or Koto CD
Jasmine or Lavender Bath Oil

sometimes DesiRe Has a DRESS CODE

Sex is fun—so your after-hours wardrobe should be full of wild, sexy staples that add to the party. In our opinion, every Dominant Diva should own the following: one feather boa, one pair of long satin gloves, one bottle of perfume that drives him wild, one sexy toe ring, one bottle of body glitter, one tube of black lipstick, one cowboy hat, and one outrageous wig. And don't wait for Halloween to break 'em out either—these eclectic elements should absolutely be incorporated into your everyday life!

THE SET-UP

Whether you live in a small town or large city, chances are there is at least one goth or fetish club in your area. Smaller areas might simply have an "alternative" or gay bar, but that will work! The goal is to find a place where you'll be free to explore a completely different look and persona. This is a place where everyone will notice, but no one will care! Have you fantasized about wearing a rubber catsuit or a tight-fitting corset that accentuates your sexy curves? Or a short black skirt with thigh-high boots? Maybe your partner has always wanted to don a long black Matrix-like coat, or wear his studded collar out in public.

Depending on what you wear and where you go, this game can be expensive and labor-intensive. Here are the Three S's you need to focus on before your big night:

SEARCH: Before you go shopping, research various outfits online. What look have you always wanted to try? What options are available? For a list of fetish stores that we trust, check out our site at www.dominantdiva.com.

SHOP: Once you've done your homework and decided on the look that's right for you, it's time to go shopping! If you're buying your fantasy-wear online, plan ahead and shop early.

SELECT: All dressed up and no place to go? Not if we have anything to say about it! First, check out your weekly paper for alternative club choices. Then, go to our website to learn about upcoming fetish events around the country.

Game on!

This game begins when you start getting dressed, so make an event of it. Help each other get ready, and pump up some club music while you're doing so. Let him help you apply your makeup or do your hair, then do his! Boost his confidence by telling him how hot he looks.

For an added element of fun, go ahead and role-play. What are your names going to be tonight? Are you the Mistress and he's the slave—or vice-versa? Are you club kids out for a good time? Or strangers who just met? You make the call...and you create the rules. Anything goes!

Once you arrive at your club of choice, your new look will do all of the work. Notice how strangers look at you differently. Revel in the attention. Do all these stares make you feel like a celebrity? Do you catch yourself looking at your man in a whole new light? That's the goal here—to try on different personas in order to fuel your fire.

So get on the dance floor and grind your guy. Buy him a drink. Slip him the tongue at the bar. Be slutty and naughty, Diva! After all, going out on the town like this is strictly foreplay. The main event will be when you get him home for some raw, passionate sex!

DRESS FOR DISTRESS

Now that you've got that Dominant Diva attitude down, it's time to walk the walk and talk the talk. That means you're going to a real-life fetish club or alternative bar in all your gothic glory. (Go, Diva!)

PASSION PROPS

Two Outrageous Outfits
One Fetish Club Destination

DRESS FOR DISTRESS

You are wearing an outfit more outrageous than you've ever worn in a bar that's more outrageous than you've ever visited. What will happen next?

⤴⤴⤴⤴$$$(

BOY
TOY

He's sexy as hell but dumb as a rock. As long as he looks good on your arm, nothing else matters!

♪♪$$$(

THE SET-UP

Send him an e-mail today that states: *I am taking you out tonight. Meet me at the house directly after work.* When he gets home, tell him that he is not allowed to say a word and that you are in charge. Explain that you're going to dress him up this evening, and you would like for everyone to see him as your boy toy.

Go into his closet and take out your favorite tight jeans, sexy briefs, and that button-down that really brings out his eyes. Select the one outfit you think makes your man look his very best (even if it's one that you like but he doesn't)! Tonight, you will enjoy seeing all eyes on him. Under no circumstances is he allowed to dress himself. You will dress him as if he were a mannequin or doll!

As you head out, open all the doors for him, reminding him that you are in charge. You are not only in control of his attire—you're in control of the entire evening! Any time you take on a task or mannerism that a man would usually master, you are boosting your power position. You might look demure and sexy in your little black dress, but you are opening car doors and calling all the shots. You are one very Dominant Diva, living large and in charge!

Game On!

Don't even let him think about driving—and don't tell him where you're going, either. Right now, the facts are on a need-to-know basis! And your boy toy doesn't need to know a thing.

Drive him straight to the nicest restaurant in town. Once you arrive, open all doors for him and announce your arrival to the maitre d'. If he's in a jacket, be sure and take it off for him before he sits down, and pull out his chair while you're at it. Order some drinks, then toast to his good looks. When the waiter gives him a menu, take it from your boy toy and tell him that you will be ordering for him this evening. Whisper that when you get back home, you are going to rip off his clothes and ravage his body. Objectify him! Be sure to look around the dining room to see if any of the other patrons are checking out the hot item you have sitting at your table tonight.

After dinner, reach over and stroke him under the table until he's good and hard. Then, when the waiter asks if you want to finish with dessert, look at your boy toy and tell him that *he's* your last course.

BOY
TOY

News flash: Your lover has just had a lobotomy. He's not allowed to use his brain for the next several hours. That's because you're his sugar mama and he's the object of your desire. You don't want him to think—you just want him to look good and satisfy you! And the best part? You call all the shots.

Passion Props

One Hot "Boy Toy" Outfit
One Dinner Reservation

THE EYES ARE
the WINDOW to the SOUL

According to tantric sex enthusiasts, looking into your partner's eyes during lovemaking is essential. They believe that eyes-open sex allows sexual energy to flow and encourages you to connect with your lover on a deeper, more soulful level. Dominant Divas are into eye contact as well. A hard stare lets him know that you're absolutely in charge. An intimate gaze fills him with that warm, I'm-so-in-love glow. And when you're staring deeply into each other's eyes at the moment of orgasm, both Os somehow feel that much more explosive.

THE set-up

When your lover arrives, hand her the following note, then ask her to read it aloud. Try not to get too excited as she reads:

The man standing in front of you is my husband. He is a wonderful man, yet he doesn't know how to please me sexually. I often find myself dissatisfied after an evening of lovemaking. I cannot tell you all the details...but let's just say that you and I have shared one other lover in our lifetime, and you had him first. By the time he met me, he had all of the skills of a sensitive, attentive, and graceful lover. One night, he confided that he had learned his love lessons from a very special woman in his past: you! I come to you now and ask that you take my husband into your bed and teach him how to please. Teach him every sexual technique you know. Let him feast on your flesh so he may later feast on mine.

Does this turn you on? I hope so. I expect you will gain as much pleasure from these love lessons as my husband will. If he for some reason disobeys, you have my permission to use any means necessary to make him a better lover. I put all my trust and faith in you without jealousy or resentment. I do not consider this cheating, as my own relationship will be strengthened as a result.

I ask one last thing of you: When you have finished with my husband tonight, please write me a note to let me know how things went. I will have a hard time believing anything that my husband says about your encounter, as he will only be interested in making himself look good. Please tell me all of the lessons he learned, and the areas in which he needs work so that I can continue his studies at home. If he needs another lesson, please let me know that as well, and I will send him back to you. Thank you.

Game on!

She may very well be shocked to receive such a letter, so you should jump in there to help. Offer your services immediately. Ask her what she would like you to do first. Anything at all! You wouldn't want this sexy stranger to pursue unnecessary measures just so you can learn how to please a woman. And you wouldn't want her to discipline you for being inadequate, would you?

So go ahead—follow her every instruction. Tonight it is all about her, and if she wants you to give her oral pleasure, an erotic massage, or hours of unbridled lovemaking, then do it. Just remember: This woman will be giving your Diva a full report on your performance, so give it your all! During your love lesson, pay special attention to the things your lover tells you to do to her. Always wondered how lightly (or roughly) she likes to be touched down there? This is the perfect opportunity to speak up and ask.

Once you are properly schooled in the ways of love, your tantric tutor will write a letter to "your wife," seal it and give it to you for safekeeping. Tomorrow night, open her naughty note to see how you rated. Read it aloud to your lover. Then get ready for another love lesson... and pray for mounds of homework!

LOVE
Lessons

Surprise! You are going back to school. The subject: a refresher course on the language of love. Ask your Goddess to meet you in the bedroom at 9 p.m. and explain that you have something special to give her.

Passion Props

One Handwritten Note
One Sincere Reply

LOVE
Lessons

men's ROOM

Ever wish your Diva would just tell you exactly what she wants? Your wish is our command, with a little help from one very hot teacher....

LiGHtS OUt

You're going to flash her tonight...

and shine a spotlight on seduction!

Ready to make her see the light?

THE SET-UP

Hide the flashlights under the bed early in the evening—and make sure both are loaded with fresh batteries. Who knows how many hours you'll need this love light? It'd be a shame for the batteries to die on you smack-dab in the middle of your carnal passion. Make sure it's pitch dark before you hit the sheets tonight. Then make your move.

Game on!

Kiss her lovingly. Nuzzle her neck. Tell her how amazing she feels. Now tell her you've got a present for her…and it's nice and long and hard…and she knows just how to turn it on. Of course, she'll instantly reach for your love rod. (What else?) But grab her hand and give her the flashlight instead. Just don't turn it on yet. Tell her you're going to use yours on her first.

Say, "I want to see all of you, every part of you, up close and personal." Shine the light on her face. Whisper, "You're so beautiful!" Kiss her. Worship her features. Study her full lips. Her gorgeous eyes. The neck…how long and graceful. Shine the light on it and appreciate its beauty.

Now shine the light on her breasts. First, the right, then the left. As you illuminate her awesome orbs, lick them. Kiss them. Nibble them. See how each nipple hardens at your touch. Study it. Again, worship it. Tell her how amazing it looks under the light. Under this intense beam, her breast is the only thing you can see in the pitch-black bedroom. It could belong to anyone—and of course, that's a fantasy in itself. But it's hers and only hers.

Shine the light on her face again and give her a deep, wet kiss. Let her know that she's the one who lights your fire. Focus on that beautiful belly button—kiss it, lick it, flick it with your tongue. Now turn the spotlight to her love lips. Shine the light close. Inspect her clitoris. Admire her vulva. Memorize its every fold. Inhale her scent. Worship her mound.

Light her love lips. Then kiss them. Tease them with the flashlight by rubbing it against her opening. Then shine the light on your penis, and let her see how hard it is. Enter her.

Now, it's her turn. Tell her to turn on her flashlight and watch you do her.

It's a sight she'll never forget.

Future variation: try the flashlight technique outside—
even if it's only in the backyard. Let your flashlights illuminate the
path to passion! Then tell her to shine her flashlight on the
areas she wants you to lick. next, make her shine the light
on the areas where she wants to lick you....

LIGHTS OUT

Just picture a single beam of light in the darkness, shining on one body part…a breast, a nipple, her luscious love lips. Under the spotlight, she feels like a movie star. Famous. The only person in the world who matters.

That's why tonight we're arming you with two flashlights—one for you, one for her.

PASSION PROPS

Two Flashlights
Fresh Batteries

CHILL to THRILL

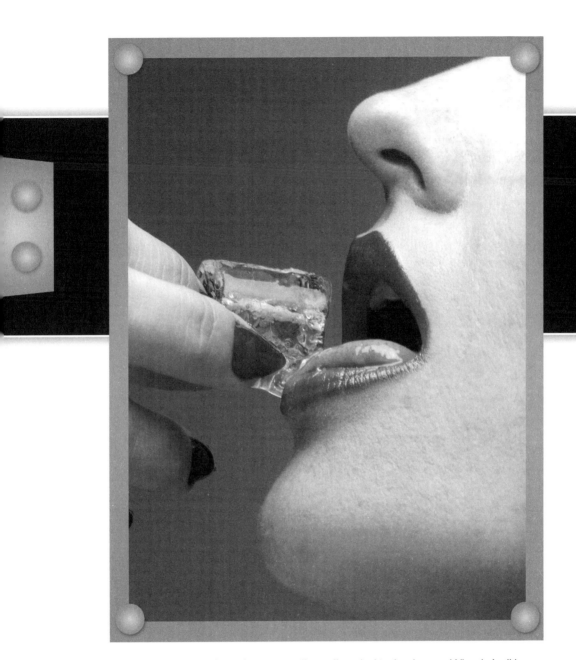

Cooling your guy down during sex will actually make him last longer. When he's all hot and sweaty, even the slightest touch of an ice cube will shock his system and pull him back from the brink of orgasm. Ice can also electrify his nerve endings and even give him goose bumps!

THE SET-UP

Make plans with your man to go on a camping trip, but don't reveal what kinky treats you have in store. Depending on your schedule, you can plan something as extravagant as a weekend away or as simple as an evening campfire in the backyard. As long as you have complete solitude, you're good to go!

Now you just need to pack a secret stash that includes a collar, ropes, and blindfold. Pack a cooler full of marshmallows, graham crackers, chocolate bars, chips, turkey dogs, potato salad, and whipped cream as well. But don't let him peek inside!

Game On!

Once the fire is roaring and your tent is all set up, tell your man that you're feeling frisky and would like to play a guessing game with him. Now, open your secret bag of goodies. Tell him to sit by the fire as you place the collar around his neck. Let him know that you have plans for him out here in the "woods" (even if you're in your own backyard), and he would be well advised to follow all of your instructions—especially if he wants to eat dinner tonight. First, lead him to a tree and tell him to face it. Next, take out the blindfold and secure it tightly over his eyes. Take your rope and tie his hands around the tree. His bum should be facing you. Tell him that you are going to place a portion of tonight's dinner under his nose. He will then be asked to identify each savory selection. If he guesses correctly, he'll be rewarded with a "reach around" hand-job as well as a bite of the delicious dinner. If he guesses incorrectly, he will be spanked with a switch for being such a bad camp slave. Psyche him out: Stomp loudly into the woods to tear off a wooden branch, all the while explaining how badly a good switching hurts. Your man's butt is already facing you, so you've got easy access! All you'll have to do is unzip his pants and expose his butt or his jewel, depending on his level of accuracy. Will he be spanked or have his monkey spanked? His fate's in his own hands...as long as he follows his nose!

Let the games begin! First, roast a marshmallow and place it directly under his nostrils. Marshmallows don't really smell like anything, so this should be a challenge for him. If he guesses wrong, give him five swipes with your switch—but if he answers correctly, stroke his penis at least five times. Ahhh...it won't take him long to realize there's a thin line between heaven and hell here! Next, roast some s'mores and give him a whiff. Up the ante each time. If he gives you the wrong response, you'll give him one more switch, but if he gives you the right response, you'll give him one more stroke. This game can go on for as long as you like. Quiz him on any of your favorite camp snacking staples, such as chips, turkey dogs, or potato salad.

No matter what happens, we can guess what he is: rock hard and ready to pounce! Once the game's over, your fun has just begun. There's nothing like outdoor camping sex to get your fires burning.

KINKY camping

Ready to pack up the tent, grill and sleeping bags for a couples-only camping extravaganza? Well, this is kinky camping; so don't forget to add a collar, blindfold, and ropes! The great outdoors has never been this wild before....

Passion Props

Ice Chest • Collar
Blindfold • Ropes • Tent
Camping Food

KINKY
CAMPING

Ready for some outdoor action?
After all, he's never had any trouble
"pitching a tent" whenever you
are around!

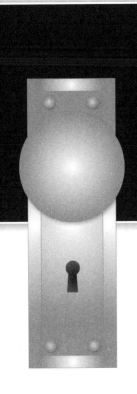

sense and sensibility

He can't touch you. He can't hear you. And he can't see you. But somehow his senses have never felt more alive....

♪♪♪♪$

THE Set-UP

Assemble all your necessary props and call him into the bedroom. Command him to disrobe and lie down on the bed face up.

Game on!

Let him know that you are about to take away three of his senses—one by one.

1) **TOUCH:** Use scarves, handcuffs, or rope to tie his hands over his head and spread his legs apart. If you're lucky enough to have a four-poster bed, tie each limb to a bedpost. Otherwise, secure the restraints to the legs of your bed frame.

2) **SIGHT:** Blindfold him so that he can't see a thing.

3) **HEARING:** Place headphones over his ears, blasting jazz, classical, or electronica music from your iPod or portable CD player.

Now that you have taken away these senses, he won't be able to see or hear what you are about to do to him, nor will he be able to stop you. In essence, you have taken all responsibility away from him—so he just gets to sit back and enjoy! You have him right where you want him, so we challenge you to use every item listed below in the most creative of ways....

- Feather duster
- Sandpaper
- Nail file
- Ice
- Vibrator
- Honey
- Whipped cream
- Shoelace
- Fingernails
- Hot sauce (for tasting purposes only)
- Warm baby oil (heated in the microwave a few seconds max—but test on your skin first)

Use these passion props to play mind games with your man. For instance, spread honey on his mouth and command him to lick it off. Then put a small amount of hot sauce in the same place! Because he won't expect to taste heat after the sweet, this will really screw with his head. Or, massage warm baby oil into his testicles then ice them down immediately after. In this game, opposite sensations pack a big punch, so get creative!

Your goal here is not to hurt him but to surprise him. Make him wonder what you're going to do next. Lightly run a nail file over his nipples. Tickle his thighs with a feather duster. Crawl on top of him and use him for your own personal pleasure! Continue screwing with his senses as you make love. Because he cannot see, hear or touch you, you have all of the power. Use it, Diva!

GODDESS TIP: TO KICK THIS GAME UP A NOTCH, WE DOUBLE DARE YOU TO PURCHASE THE FOLLOWING TOYS BEFOREHAND. BOTH ARE S/M CLASSICS: PINWHEEL: A ROLLING PINWHEEL OF SHARP METAL POINTS (WWW.GOODVIBES.COM) CLOTHESPINS: PERFECT FOR GIVING HIS INNER THIGHS A PASSION PINCH!

sense and sensibility

This game begins with the usual suspects: erotic ambiance, slinky attire for a sexy Diva, and a man willing to serve. But there is a fill-in-the-blank element to the game where you'll get the chance to let your own ingenuity shine through. Be devious, Diva!

passion props

Rope, Scarves, or Handcuffs
Blindfold • Headphones with
iPod or Portable CD Player
Erotic Toys

BRING HIM to HIS KNEES

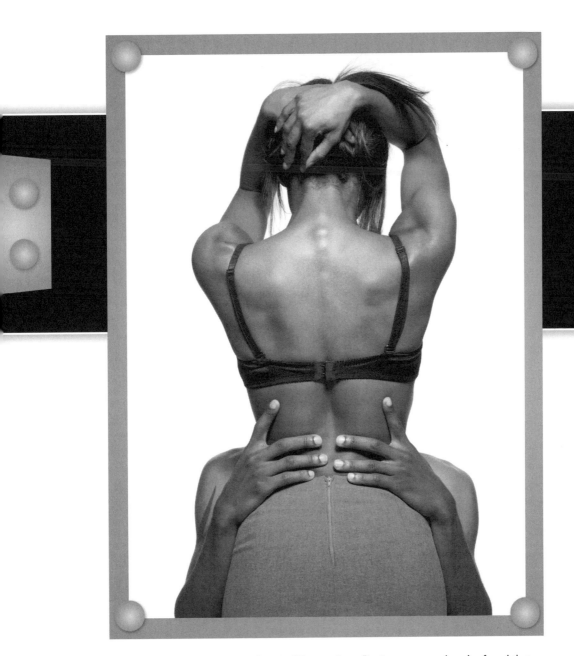

Receiving oral pleasure is a favorite Diva pastime. But in our research we've found that many women won't even allow their guys to go down on them. Why? They're just not confident enough with their bodies to let their main men hang out down south. But we say if he's into you, he's into all of you—and that includes your luscious love lips. So let him give them the attention they deserve, and throw those hang-ups out the window. You're lovable, Diva…every incredible inch!

THE SET-UP

He can't have an O, but it's your mission to try your hardest to make him have one! First, gather any and all ammunition you can think of: sex toys, pornos, girlie mags, your sexiest lingerie. Pull out all the stops! Then sit down and hatch your five-night plan. Make sure each night will be different from the last. Incorporate all his biggest turn-ons in hopes of making him blow a gasket!

GAME ON!

Explain the ground rules. You are allowed to do whatever you want to him sexually Monday through Friday, and the only time he can tell you to stop is when he's nearing orgasm. Before the game, ask him to write down his sexual reward of choice, and then place it in a sealed envelope. Simultaneously write down the punishment you've planned for him, and place that in a second sealed envelope. Stash them both away for safekeeping.

As you know, the key to your victory lies in concocting difficult sexual obstacles for your guy to overcome. Be ruthless! If he gets weak in the knees over a certain porno, pop it into the DVD player on the first night! On night two, give him a 60-second hand-job before bed to get him riled. You get the picture....

Throughout the week, tease each other about the punishments and rewards. For instance, taunt him by saying, "I can't wait until you cave, because you are going to pay big-time!" He might exclaim, "Saturday's going to be the best night of my life!" Egg each other on to up the erotic ante!

Saturday is payday. After a candlelit dinner, open the envelopes together. If you succeeded in pushing him over the brink at some point during the week, you'll get to inflict his punishment after dessert. But if your man showed Herculean effort and actually abstained from blasting off, you'll be fulfilling his sexual fantasy instead.

GODDESS TIP: WHEN CONCOCTING HIS PUNISHMENT, BE CREATIVE! MAYBE YOU'LL BEND HIM OVER YOUR KNEE AND GIVE HIM TWENTY SWATS. OR FORCE HIM TO GIVE YOU ORAL FOR A FULL THIRTY MINUTES. OR MAKE HIM WATCH A CHICK FLICK WITH YOU WITHOUT ONCE COMPLAINING OR CRINGING. YOU KNOW HIS LIKES AND DISLIKES BETTER THAN ANYONE, SO PLAN YOUR PUNISHMENT ACCORDINGLY! WHAT'S REALLY GONNA GET UNDER HIS SKIN?!

CLIMAX CONTROL

Do you Divas know how often your partner masturbates? We would be willing to bet he waxes the carrot way more than you realize. But shouldn't all that pent-up sexual energy be saved just for you? This Monday, put him on an orgasm embargo. He's not allowed to release Monday through Friday. If you push him over the erotic edge before Saturday morning, he will be punished. But if he holds out, you'll reward him by fulfilling the sexual fantasy of his choice. (Diva-approved, of course!)

Passion Props

Sex Toys • Pornos
Girlie Magazines
Lingerie

CLIMAX CONTROL

Surviving five days without an orgasm certainly isn't easy. But the longer you wait for something, the sweeter it is in the end....

♪♪$

Strangers in the Night

Whoa—check out that smoking hot guy who's sidled up to the bar! You've gotta get a piece of that!

⌐⌐⌐$(

THE SET-UP

Arrange to meet at a bar or party in different cars. The catch: You don't know each other. Wear a tight black dress, spiked stilettos, and black stockings. Spend some extra time on your hair and makeup, too. Tonight's your night to shine, Diva!

Game on!

When you see your man walk in, catch his gaze. You are a strong and sexy femme fatale, and you're not afraid to make the first move. Send him a drink just to show that you're interested, but don't approach him right away. Instead, visit with friends or just quietly and confidently enjoy your drink. He'll be dying for you to come over and "introduce" yourself, but hold back. Make him sweat!

After you've made him squirm (and yearn), it's time to approach your prey. Your every mannerism should mimic the typical male's here. Think back to the last time you were picked up in a bar. Did the guy buy you a drink, feed you endless compliments, and/or brag about his own accomplishments just to impress you? Sure, it was obvious he just wanted to get laid, but he went through the requisite song and dance to try and woo you. Tonight, the roles are reversed and you are on the prowl for one thing and one thing only: a night of unbridled, passionate sex with this gorgeous stranger!

Give him your best pickup line. Run your fingers along his upper arm (as he flexes those muscles). Tell him how hot he is. Bat your eyelashes. Flip your hair back. Flirt shamelessly!

Create an outrageous back story. Maybe you ran with the bulls in Spain. Were a roadie for a rock band. Or modeled for a lingerie company. Wow him with your accomplishments!

Once he's under your spell, ask him if he would like to come home with you. When you get back to the house, offer him a seat on the couch. Lean in for a kiss, and slip him the tongue. Stroke the growing bulge under his jeans. Once he's nice and hard, warn him how dangerous it is to go home with a complete stranger. Then prove it: Take him to the bedroom and strap him down with your handcuffs. He really should be more careful next time! Now he has no choice but to relax and enjoy the ride....

Use this stranger for your pleasure until you hit your O, Diva! Once you've used and abused him, release him from the cuffs. Tell him it's been very nice meeting him, but you really need to get your beauty sleep. Would he mind showing himself out?

strangers in the night

How often do you and your man go to parties? This hot role-play game is just perfect for a swanky soiree with friends! Not much of a socialite? This scene could also play out in your favorite bar. But wherever you go, keep it real! Stay in character throughout the night from beginning to end. If you both buy into what's happening, the sex will seriously sizzle....

passion props

One Bar or Party Destination
Two Cars • Handcuffs

Be HIS Damsel in DISTRESS

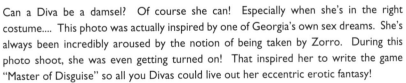

Can a Diva be a damsel? Of course she can! Especially when she's in the right costume.... This photo was actually inspired by one of Georgia's own sex dreams. She's always been incredibly aroused by the notion of being taken by Zorro. During this photo shoot, she was even getting turned on! That inspired her to write the game "Master of Disguise" so all you Divas could live out her eccentric erotic fantasy!

THE SET-UP

Time to go shopping! Most every town has a local costume shop, and there are plenty of them online. Check out www.versatile-fashions.com for more exotic characters or the fabulous www.hollywoodcostumesandparty.com for your choice of adult or traditional costumes. The Hollywood Costumes and Party website has the most extensive list of costumes we've ever seen, so we recommend checking that site out first. Costume shops and sites such as these often feature sexy costumes for seemingly innocent characters. Snow White, Little Miss Muffet, and Sleeping Beauty have never looked so sizzling! Some of the guys' costumes are pretty skimpy, too—but there is something for everyone of all shapes and sizes.

Got the costumes? Good! This game is best played if you take turns: He dresses up one night, you dress up the next. This way, you'll each get equal focus. Plus, this strategy gives you two nights of hot sex instead of one!

GAME ON!

Create the right atmosphere for the character who is taking center stage. For example, if he's dressed as Zorro, place candles around the room and scatter flower petals on and around the bed. Spanish music is an absolute must. When he makes his grand entrance (resplendent in cape and sword), allow this masked marvel to seduce you. Be sure to stay in character during the foreplay as well as the intercourse. Let yourself go!

When it's your turn to dress up, get into it! If you're dressing as Wonder Woman, for instance, tie him up with the lasso of truth and make him confess his undying desire for you before you have your way with him. The goal here is to just throw yourself into the silliness of the situation and leave your inhibitions at the door.

If you can't resist the temptation of both dressing up at once, why not choose complementary characters such as Han Solo and Princess Leia? (*Star Wars* sex is outta this world—literally!) Or transform into an Arabian prince and exotic belly dancer. Decorate your bedroom in colorful silks and fabrics, candles glowing in every corner. Feast on wine and grapes with your prince until he decides to take you as his sex slave....

The possibilities here are indeed endless. Playing fictional characters between the sheets allows you to take your role-play games to a whole new level. And the best part? When Halloween comes around, you'll already have your costumes!

GODDESS TIP: ON A BUDGET?
PLAY THIS GAME RIGHT AFTER HALLOWEEN,
WHEN MOST COSTUMES ARE 50-75% OFF!

master OF DISGUISE

Have you ever secretly fantasized about Zorro between the sheets or longed for a late night visit from Count Dracula? Maybe your guy's always secretly wondered what it'd be like to sleep with Catwoman. Or does Wonder Woman hold a special place in his heart? Very soon, you and your man will be going on an exciting shopping trip. Your mission: to choose costumes for each other, then make love as those larger-than-life characters!

PASSION PROPS

Two Costumes

master OF DISGUISE

Your guy's always been your superhero in the bedroom...so now it's
time for him to start dressing the
part. Look! It's a bird, it's a plane,
it's...Superstud!

◢◢◢$$

Den OF
sin

You most definitely have a princess complex. And when you enter this palace, you'll be royally screwed!

⌐⌐⌐$$

THE SET-UP

Your first royal duty is to turn your bedroom into a boudoir. Stop by your local fabric store and purchase several yards of silk and fake fur fabrics that are bright, exotic, and soft to the touch. Be sure to buy one piece of fabric that's large enough to drape over your mattress and pillows. Then scatter the rest of the remnants around your room. Your old drab bedroom will cease to exist under all the colorful silks!

Light incense and candles around the bed, and play some Middle Eastern music to set the mood. Stash some white wine and strawberries nearby, put on a simple robe, and you're good to go.

Game on!

When your sex slave enters the room, make him take all his clothes off. Gaze at his gorgeous flesh glistening in the candlelight as you loosely wrap him in a bolt of the silky fabric.

Explain his new role as your sex slave. His mission is to do exactly as he is told in order to please you.

Using your passion props, you will now awaken each of your man's senses one by one. First, you must tantalize his sense of touch. Make him rub the tactile silks and furs on all—and we do mean all—of his erogenous zones. As he gratifies himself in front of you, tell him to take a big whiff of the sweet-smelling incense. Then ask him to listen to the haunting Middle Eastern music and rub himself to the beat. This should send his senses into absolute overload!

But there's one very important sense left: taste! This just might be the most erotic of them all.

Lead your slave to the bed and blindfold him with one of the fabrics. Then run the fur up and down his body, teasing his manhood with the supple softness. Feed him strawberries and wine, gently reminding him that he would normally be feeding you. Sex slaves never get preferential treatment, so he obviously owes you a proper thank you. Suggest he show his gratitude by tasting and licking your luscious mound. Make sure he thanks you for the privilege of doing so! If he's skilled enough with his tongue, allow him to mount you before beckoning the rest of your harem.

Now really take what is yours, princess. Remove his blindfold, then bend over doggie style and command him to enter you. He is a sex slave and it is his duty to please the princess! Get lost in your palatial surroundings until you both reach orgasm in this erotic and exotic place.

Den of
sin

Tonight, you are a princess who has her sights set on a sexy slave boy. To satisfy your every whim, this manly hunk of flesh must feed you wine and strawberries and lick you in all the right places. Now this is what you call *slave labor*....

Passion Props

Silky Fabric • Furry Fabric
Incense • Candles • Wine
Middle Eastern Music
Strawberries • Blindfold

come out ON TOP!

The ultraempowering "female superior position" sends women into pleasure heaven for many reasons. First, it allows the man to penetrate his Diva even deeper, which feels good for both parties involved. Being on top also gives the woman control over the speed and depth of lovemaking—which is a wonderful way to manipulate his love muscle. Need one more reason to hop on top? Researchers recently found that the majority of women who reliably have Os during intercourse are positioned on top—so increase your odds of orgasm by straddling your sweetie tonight!

THE SET-UP

Two hours before your date, hand him a note that reads something like this:

We are heading to our first destination at 7 p.m. That leaves us two full hours to get ready—and we will need every millisecond! I would like you to walk directly into my bedroom and lay out my clothes: a black cocktail dress, lacy panties, and black pumps. Once you're done, draw me a nice warm bath. After you have pampered and bathed me, you will dry me off and dress me. While I put on my makeup, you'll serve me a glass of wine. Then I'll choose your chauffeur uniform for this evening. Once I have decided that you are presentable, we will be on our way.

But there are some ground rules:
1) While we get ready, you are not allowed to speak unless spoken to.
2) You are to open all doors for me.
3) You will chauffeur me wherever I desire.

Game on!

At 7 p.m. sharp, get in the backseat and make him chauffeur you to a sex shop. Make him wait in the car with the engine running as you dash in and buy yourself a new vibe. Slip it in your purse so he can't see. He'll wonder what tantalizing toy you purchased, but no matter how much he begs, don't tell!

Instead, tell him to drive directly to the fanciest hotel in town. He'll probably wonder if you're getting a room—but the hotel bar is where you're headed. Order two stiff drinks, then make him stiff, too, by rubbing his knee and his thigh teasingly.

Excuse yourself and head for the ladies' room. Slip those batteries into your new vibrator. You'll need that power surge shortly.

After you return from the loo and finish your drink, take a ballpoint pen and write an address on the back of your chauffeur's hand. It's the address of a cheap hotel nearby—but he doesn't know that. Just tell him to drive you there. Again, hop in the backseat while your chauffeur takes you to your destination. Pull your vibrator out of your purse and let him hear the love buzz as you rub it along your clit. Explain how good it feels and how much you wish he could touch you, too.

When he pulls up to the seedy hotel, tell him to go in and get a room. Make him ask the clerk if they rent rooms by the hour—because you'll only need the place for 60 minutes tops. That's more than enough time for you to rock his freaking world!

Once you enter your sin suite, go primal! Do him on the bed, on the desk, on the floor…in every position you can think of. Talk dirty. Shag like rock stars. Make history.

DRIVING
MISS DIVA

Ready to hit the road with your man? Let him know ahead of time that he must clear Saturday night for you. You'll have some prep work for him to do, so he needs to meet you at 5 p.m. that night for further instructions....

Passion Props

Black Cocktail Dress
High Heels • Lacy Panties
Car • Vibrator • Batteries

DRIVING
miss DIVa

He's the chauffeur who drives you
everywhere you want to go. Now,
it's your turn to drive him...wild!

♪♪♪♪$$(

DOUBLE TROUBLE

He's ordering another girl drinks, taking her out to dinner, pulling out her chair—and you're totally cool with it. What gives?

⌁⌁⌁$$(

THe set-UP

Remember back in the day when you and your best girlfriend would go out and get crazy together? Those times were simply scandalous! But now that you're with your man, we bet those girls' nights out have grown fewer and farther between. Hey, it happens. But why not revive your old tradition and include your man in your plans? He can pick up the tab, check the coats, and fetch the drinks! By the end of the night, your gal pal will not only envy your relationship, she'll wonder how she can get such an attentive guy of her own! She'll marvel over the fact that a man could possibly be so giving. But what she doesn't know is that for all this giving, he'll be doing a lot of *getting* later on!

Tell your guy what's up. Tonight, he's your man servant, and he'll be taking you and your best friend out on the town. If he caters to your every whim, you'll give him the BJ of his life when you get home. That should be all the incentive he needs....

Game on!

Start off your evening by asking him to pick up both you and your friend from work. Where are your dinner reservations? Your guy will happily take you there, pull out your chairs, and pick up the tab. With two Divas to attend to, he probably won't get a word in edgewise during dinner—but that's fine by him. He'll just be there on standby, ready and willing to accommodate any request you might have. What a good boy!

Whatever you do, don't let your friend in on your little secret. Exposing or humiliating your man in front of others is demeaning, not desirable. Just let her think he's the sweetest, most attentive guy in the world (which is totally true)!

After dinner, ask your guy to take you to a rockin' nightclub. Make him dance with you and your girlfriend. Get crazy, just like the good ol' days!

But don't stay out too late, Diva! You have some matters to attend to when you get home.

GODDESS TIP: FOR FUTURE VARIATION, ASK YOUR GUY TO
GO OUT WITH A GROUP OF YOUR GIRLFRIENDS. HE'LL FEEL LIKE
HUGH HEFNER SURROUNDED BY ALL THOSE DIVAS!

DOUBLE TROUBLE

Every time you hang out with your girlfriends, they always ask how it's going with your man. So why not bring him along next time to show him off to the girls?

Passion Props

One Best Friend
Dinner Reservations
Nightclub Destination

CREATE A SEX SOUNDTRACK

Introducing sounds into your lovemaking will undoubtedly add a new dimension to your between-the-sheets action. Music, dirty talk, or erotic bedtime stories all have the ability to pump up the volume of your passion!

THE SET-UP

The object of this game is to find and download erotic short stories into your iPod or MP3 player to drive him wild! (The other alternative would be to download the stories onto your computer, then burn them to CD.) There are many online resources that offer audio books for downloading. We've had great success with www.audible.com, a website dedicated to audio books for download or purchase. Go to the website and do a search on "erotica." They offer tons of hot selections, and even allow you to sample the stories before purchase. There is something for everyone—straight sex, one-night stands, public encounters…you name it, they've got it! The audio books last from one to eight hours and cost anywhere from $12 to $25. Or go to our site at www.dominantdiva.com for a cherry-picked list of our favorite short stories. Most last just a half-hour or less and cost under $10.

GAME ON!

Now that you've got the sounds, it's time to select the setting. Does your man use his iPod at the gym? Leave a Post-It on the player saying, "These stories will REALLY make you sweat!" Does he listen to music on his way to work? Sneak out to his car and replace his CD of choice with a little erotic cliterature!

Or create some great groin tension on his way home: Tell him you've got something special for him to listen to at the end of a long, hard day (emphasis on *long* and *hard*)! Call his cell to make sure he is doing his "homework," then casually mention you're listening to the same stories right this very second—and touching yourself! He'll be so eager to get home, it will be a miracle if he doesn't get a speeding ticket. Vroom, vroom!

Is he going away on a business trip anytime soon? Borrow his iPod the night before his departure and download a few suggestive stories. On the morning of his trip, tell him he's in for a sexy surprise. Your only request is that he listen to his iPod during the flight. Once he hears these titillating tales at 30,000 feet, he won't know what hit him. Let's hope the airline provides blankets: To hide his hard-on, he just might need two!

Once you're reunited, reenact the sexy stories together—then make him listen to the iPod while you rub his bod!

ear
candy

Unless you've been living under a rock, you know that iPods and MP3 players are essential to 21st century life. So why not use these technically advanced toys to sexually advance your sex life, too?

(Don't have one? No worries: You can easily use CDs instead!)

Passion Props

Computer • Erotic MP3 File
CD Player or iPod

ear candy

Did you know his ears can be one of your man's most sensitive erogenous zones? When you treat him to this sexy surprise, you'll turn him on from his head to...well, his *other* head!

LaptoP LUSt

Wanna see two strangers get it on? Ever fantasized about spying on another couple's sexcapades? Well, you're in luck. It's time to peek through the peephole of pleasure.

THE SeT-UP

There are two basic types of sex webcam sites, so first you need to select the right one for you. A member's site averages $15 a month, and gives you access to thousands of photos, stories, and archived sex scenes that can be downloaded for your viewing pleasure. Live sites offer streaming real-time sex shows you can pay to watch on a one-time basis. A sex show normally costs $15-$20, and is an interactive experience. This means you can "partici-pate" by typing in sex acts for the lovers to act out. There are countless websites to choose from, so refer to ours (www.dominantdiva.com) for a list of ones that have earned our stamp of approval.

Game on!

We've given you two games to choose from—a wild side and a mild side. Choose the one that turns you on most, or double your pleasure and do both!

GODDeSS Game 1: WiLD SiDe

If you've selected a live sex show, pour yourself a few cocktails 10 minutes before the performance, log on and settle down in front of the computer with your man. You don't want to miss a minute! Once the action begins, jump right in and make a sexual request. Don't worry—you're totally anonymous here, so there's no need to be shy. For example, if you are spying on a dominatrix spanking her slave, and you would like to see her pull his hair, ask and you shall receive. This really is the next best thing to being there! Watching a straight sex scene? Go ahead—ask the hot guy to touch himself! Anything goes here....

It won't be long before the on-screen action has your own juices flowing. That's your cue to initiate your own live sex scene with your man. Let the actors in on the fun by typing in a naughty message such as: "You're getting us so turned on, we're having sex right here in front of the computer!" Act like they're watching you, too!

GODDeSS Game 2: miLD SiDe

Opted for an archived scene? Sit on your man's lap in front of the computer and pretend that it's live! Ask your guy if he likes it when the girl goes down on her man or gives him a hand-job. Would he like you to do that to him, too? Use this scene as an inspiration for your own sexual adventures by mimicking the action on your monitor. We bet you'll sizzle more than the porn stars do!

Laptop Lust

Have you or your partner ever secretly (or not-so-secretly) wanted
to watch a live sex show? Well,
thanks to the World Wide Web,
you can now do so without leaving
the comfort of your own home!

Passion Props

Computer
Sex Site

IF THE
SHOE FITS...

Black heels are so sexy! Wear yours tonight with your naughtiest lingerie. The stilettos will make your calves appear more shapely and your legs look even longer. Then have sex with your shoes on. If you make love standing up, the extra height will give you new sensations—and give him a little extra thrust!

THE SET-UP

Send your lover to the bedroom and ask him to strip down. He is then to lie on his back on the floor at the foot of the bed. From that angle, he'll likely spy your new stilettos. Enter the room in a simple robe, wearing nothing underneath. Point out the newest addition to your shoe collection.

Game on!

Take the robe off and reveal your gorgeous body. Spread your legs and stand over his face so he can admire your love lips. Tower over him! Once he has soaked in your beauty, take a seat on the bed, allowing your bare feet to lazily rest on his torso. Lightly drag one of your feet down to his manhood and stroke him with it. During this foot job, tell your guy that he's now in training to be your footstool!

Lean down and pick up your stilettos. Put your heels on in front of him and rest them on his torso. Using the base of the shoe, apply firm pressure to his penis. Ask him if he knows who is in charge. There will be no doubt that you are definitely calling the shots!

GODDESS GAME 1: WILD SIDE

Want to take things a "step" further? Brand your boy toy with your heel marks! Fetishists call this trampling, and this is something Georgia does a lot with her clients. Standing or walking on another person is one of the most classic acts of physical dominance, but we're giving this move a Diva twist. Tell him that you would like for him to wear your heel marks on his chest tonight as a symbol of his servitude. If the marks are still noticeable in the morning, then he may request any consensual sexual favor to be acted out first thing. But if the marks are gone, he won't get any reward.

Place the heel marks on his chest by sitting on the edge of the bed and applying a fair amount of pressure on his torso. Never stand and put your full weight on his body. (Not only would this inflict an immense amount of pain, you could also cause some major damage!)

Two or three heel marks should do the trick. Immediately afterward, ease his pain by giving your guy the BJ of his life.

GODDESS GAME 2: MILD SIDE

Tease him by telling him you're going to walk all over him if he's a bad boy. Make him kiss the tips of your shoes while he touches himself. Once he's fully erect, get down on the floor and make love to him with your stilettos on. Put your best foot forward!

Heel, BOY!

You've just returned from a day of retail therapy, and boy—did you hit the jackpot! You scored a brand new pair of stilettos that are sexy as hell. There's only one problem: Because these heels are not exactly "sensible" or even comfortable, you'll need a sturdy footstool to rest your tortured tootsies. We've got something in mind....

Passion Props

One Pair of Spiked Stilettos

Heel, BOY!

Slip on your sexiest shoes. It's time

to take a walk on the wild side.

◢◢◢◢$

TAKE HIS BREATH AWAY

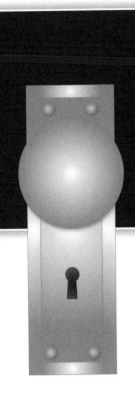

Tired, Diva? Kick back, relax, and have a seat…on his face!

THE Set-UP

First, hide a hairbrush and nail file under your pillow. Then take a long, hot shower, and put on a garter and stockings (no panties). Beckon him to the bedroom for his lust lesson. Strip all of his clothes off and make him lie down on the bed face up.

Game On!

Begin by getting on top of him and teasing him with your body. Ultimately, you want to end by straddling his face. Wow, what a sight to behold! The visual alone will make him melt. As you're straddling his face, ask, "Do I take your breath away?" In this compromising position, it's a given that he'll reply with a resounding "YES!"

Make him worship and lick your clit. Grind on his face, then tease him with your love lips. Make contact with his mouth, then lift up again so you're just out of his tongue's reach. Make him beg for a taste!

After he has gone down (or, in this case, up!) on you for a while, spin around so you are facing the other direction. Tell him it would please you if he'd cover your beautiful ass in kisses. Once you lower your booty to his face, again whisper, "Do I take your breath away?" Before he can reply, slowly "pin and smother" his face, leaning on his chest for balance. See, you really *do* take his breath away!

Face-sitting and forced ass-worship is a popular fetish—but the goal is to stimulate him, not smother him. Make sure he's getting enough air at all times!

Explain that your beautiful ass deserves a soft cushion underneath it, so he will now become your human chair. When you decide to lift up and give him some air, he must immediately thank you by kissing all your hottest spots! This will show his appreciation for the opportunity to serve as your "chairman."

While he kisses you in all the right places, reach over and stroke his dick as a reward! But if you don't feel he's kissing you enthusiastically enough, sit on his face for an even longer stretch the next time. (Here's where the hairbrush and nail file come into play. Drive him crazy by doing your hair or filing your nails while he struggles beneath you!) Repeat this move one or two more times until he's thoroughly learned his lesson. Then reward him for his chairmanly duties by hopping on that stiff love rod for a passionate pony ride!

Take HIS
BReath away

You've taken his breath away many times...by the incredible way you make him feel, how amazing you look, and on and on. This time, you'll take your man's breath away Diva-style!

Passion PROPS

Garter • Stockings
Hairbrush • Nail File

TAKE ONE
FOR tHE TEAM!

Role-play games that take you back in time are a turn-on for many reasons. Most of us were in hormone overload during high school, but couldn't do much about it except touch ourselves. But now, you can actually act out those high school fantasies with a ready and willing partner! (How hot is that?) Plus, these games put you back into that high school frame of mind, which naturally makes you feel 17 again....

THE SET-UP

This game will be even more fun if you let your sweetie in on your plans beforehand. First, talk about what kind of cliques you hung out with in high school. Were you a jock, stoner, or brainiac? Was she a cheerleader, skater chick, or bad girl? If you went to high school together, take a walk down memory lane and discuss your first impressions of each other.

Now, think back to a date you had when you were in high school. Your primary goal was to get some nookie from that cute girl in the tight sweater, wasn't it? Analyze how you went about it. What was your date destination? Did you take her to a scary movie in hopes that she would wrap her sweet arms around you for protection? Or head to the ice skating rink so that she'd snuggle up to you to get warm? Of course, the date always ended in a steamy make-out session in your parents' car—or at least, that's how you hoped it would end!

Tonight, you are going to take your Diva on a similar outing so you can try all your classic moves on her. But this time, that cute girl in the tight sweater might just go all the way!

Game On!

Time to pick up the hottest girl in school for your big date! (The good news: You don't have to worry about meeting her dad!) Take her wherever you took girls in high school...to the movies, the pizza joint, or even a varsity football game. During the date, try to get the nerve up to put your arm around her. Tell her how pretty she looks. Remember that discussion you had beforehand about what kind of cliques you both hung out with back in high school? Cite those specifics now: "I can't believe the class president is going out with a band geek like me...." Confess how much you've been checking her out in class. Your Diva will definitely eat up all this attention!

Once the date is drawing to a close, all you can think of is how badly you would like to get her in the backseat for just a little taste. So, on your way home, pull over to a secluded spot (even if it's your own driveway) and start fogging up those windows! Try for first base. Any luck? You'll find out soon enough if she puts out....

Whisper, "Let me feel your panties." She'll likely resist, "No, I'm not that kind of girl! I'm a virgin!" That's when you'll plead, "I promise I won't go inside your panties! Please just let me rub the outside!"

When she acquiesces, go ahead and feel just how wet she is.... "Uh, sorry, my hand slipped. But I won't go any further! I promise!" Then give in to temptation and break that promise right there in the backseat!

Ah, high school...those were the days!

BaCK IN
HIGH SCHOOL

Remember the good ol' days when you had nothing to worry about except homework, girls, and grades? There's nothing quite like that age of innocence. Take your girl on a trip back in time to relive those high school years!

PASSION PROPS

Car • Make-Out Spot
Lots of High School Memories

BACK IN
HIGH SCHOOL

men's
ROOM

Tonight, time travel really does
exist. And you are about to transform into the luckiest high school
student on earth.

◢◢$(

meet me at HALFtime

It's your turn to be the Dominant Dude. Gimme an S, gimme an E, gimme an X!

⌐⌐⌐$

THE SET-UP

You may want to buy your sweetie a cheerleader outfit for this game. She will love the fact that you put so much effort into your sexcapades! Most costume shops (either local or online) carry a wide variety of cheerleader uniforms. Don't forget to throw in some pom-poms she can hold on to while you take her from behind.

If this game gets you so hot that you have to do it RIGHT NOW, sans costume, then go for it! Just tell her to put on a tank top and miniskirt with white socks and voila: A cheerleader is born! Oh, and don't forget to tell her to put her hair in a mile-high ponytail…you'll need something to hold on to as well!

Game on!

Once she has her uniform on, dim the lights in the bedroom and pull her close to you. Tell her how hot she looked jumping around and cheering for you on the sidelines. You just couldn't take your eyes off of her perky breasts bopping up and down in that tight top! She got you so horny during halftime, you're all pent-up. And now, it's her cheerleaderly duty to help relieve all that sexual tension.

Hurry! Whip your dick out, make her get down on her knees, and stick it in her mouth. Tell her that she will be the most popular girl in school if you decide to date her. She just has to prove that she is willing to please you first. It's time to suck it like she means it. Make her really lube it up because you're ready to do her now.

Don't give her time to say or do anything! Just lift her back up off of her knees, turn her around, bend her over the bed and hike up her skirt. Pull her little cotton panties down around her ankles and diddle her. She knows she loves it! Slip your fingers in and out, really juicing her up as you prepare to take her. You notice that she is nice and wet as you enter her love lips. She looks so sexy with her skirt flipped up over her back. C'mon, Mr. Football Star, grab her ponytail as you ride her to ecstasy!

FUTURE VARIATION: DURING FOOTBALL SEASON, BUY TICKETS AND TAKE HER TO A LOCAL GAME. SHE'LL BE SURPRISED WHEN YOU PULL HER UNDER THE BLEACHERS FOR A LITTLE MAKE-OUT SESSION. COP A FEEL DURING HALFTIME AND THEN TEASE HER ABOUT HOW SHE IS GOING TO HAVE TO TAKE ONE FOR THE TEAM WHEN SHE GETS HOME.

meet me at
HALFtime

Bringing a little school spirit into the bedroom is a great way to kick off a scorching night of hot sex! You are the football hero who just won the state championship. Guess what? That stacked, slutty cheerleader on the sidelines is your ultimate trophy!

Passion Props

Cheerleader Costume
Pom-Poms

HE'LL BE WORKING
LATE TONIGHT

Do sex and the workplace mix? Most definitely! No, we're not suggesting that you have sex on your desk (although that would be pretty hot...), but leaving your guy a sexy voice mail at work or buying a sex toy on your lunch break can definitely spice up your 9-to-5 routine. Work it, Diva!

THE SeT-UP

Start by cooking him a nice meal, but don't let him into the kitchen! Not only do you have a surprise supper in store, you're cooking up a mystery evening as well. During dinner, you will be asking your guy a series of very personal questions. For each answer that he gets right, he'll be handsomely rewarded in a sexual way. But for each answer he gets wrong, he'll be punished—and will even be forced to choose his method of punishment. *Hurts so good....*

Ask him to meet you for dinner in the buff at 8 p.m. sharp. Beforehand, formulate your questions. Below, you'll find a short list of suggestions to help get your creative juices flowing.

Sample Questions
1) What am I making for dinner?
   He'll have to depend on his sense of smell for this one. If you're feeling really ruthless, you could always just make a salad, which has no scent.
2) Where did we go on our first date?
   Hope he has a good memory!
3) What was I wearing yesterday?
   His response will tell you how well he pays attention to the little details.
4) Where did we make love for the first time?
   Hopefully, that's a place he'll never forget....

Game on!

Once you've asked your first question, it's time for the punishment or reward.

If he gets it wrong, force him to choose from the following pain props:
1) Shoelace: Tie up his jewel with this.
2) Hairbrush: Run the bristles up and down his body before spanking his bottom with the other side.
3) Toothpaste: Place a little dab of gel toothpaste at the end of his penis and watch him wiggle!
4) Clothespins: Use these only on his inner thigh, but threaten to clothespin his penis, testicles, or nipples. (Ouch!)

If he gets it right, reward him with one of the following sexual favors:
1) Suck his penis for 3 minutes.
2) Give him a well-lubed hand-job.
3) Let him lick your boobs or love lips.
4) Massage and cup his balls.

After he responds to the "What am I making for dinner?" inquiry, dinner is served. Continue to fire questions at him throughout the meal, taking breaks for the punishments or rewards. Looks like this is going to be one looooooong dinner! But if he's a good boy and serves up enough right answers, he just might be eating you!

GODDESS
GAME SHOW

What a wonderful partner you have! He's so smart, kind, and attentive.... Wait a minute! Just how attentive is he? Find out by playing a game of 20 Questions and throwing in a little punishment/reward system to raise the stakes! Better yet, mix in a little something sexual—and you've got one hot game on your hands!

PASSION PROPS

Home-Cooked Meal
Shoelace • Hairbrush
Gel Toothpaste • Clothespins

GODDESS
GAME SHOW

Every man dreads those five little words: "Honey, we need to talk." But, this time, talking could be a good thing!

_⌐⌐$

sex
cells

If a picture's worth a thousand words, these photos are worth at least a million. Say "Sleaze!"

THE SET-UP

Get up a little early this morning and secretly borrow your man's cell phone. Go into the bathroom and start snapping away! Take photos of yourself fondling your breasts, touching your puss, or slapping your butt. Then save your sexy snaps in his photo gallery. Put his phone back where you found it and return to business as usual.

GAME ON!

Around lunchtime, send him a text message that says, "Hot N Horny. Bedroom date 7 p.m." Give him a few moments to fantasize about all the steamy sex he is going to get tonight before you text message him again: "Preview in phone photo gallery."

He won't be able to resist checking his gallery right then and there! When he opens those sizzling hot photos of you, he'll have to hightail it to the nearest bathroom to hide the pup tent in his pants.

If you own a cell phone that has the ability to send photos from phone to phone, why not tease him a little more by sending him a new picture? Retire to a secluded spot, snap a shot, and forward the goods! If you can, try incorporating background images in the photo. It will blow him away when he realizes you're flashing skin in a corner of the grocery store or your office cubicle! Next, text message him the Diva challenge: "Show me yours. I want wood."

The gauntlet's been thrown! Prepare to start receiving some raunchy porn shots of your own. This could turn into a real battle of the sexes. Who can snap the sexiest shot before 7 p.m.?

Bet neither one of you will be home late tonight! After all, you've had so many sneak peeks throughout the day, you're ready to see the main attraction—live, up close, and personal!

GODDESS TIP: THE NEXT TIME YOU AND YOUR MAN PURCHASE NEW CELL PHONES, BUY ONES THAT ARE EQUIPPED WITH VIDEO CLIP TECHNOLOGY. (BOTH PHONES HAVE TO COME WITH THIS FEATURE TO WORK.) THAT WAY, YOU CAN SEND HIM HIS OWN PRIVATE PEEP SHOW!

sex
cells

Camera phones are not just nov-
elties anymore—they're cheap,
user-friendly, and readily available.
It seems like everybody has one!
Today, you are going to put his
phone to good use by surprising
him with some X-rated photos.
And if all goes according to plan,
you might just get some in return.

Passion Props

Camera Phone

GIVE HIM
easy access!

Go commando every once in a while—especially if you're in public with your guy. It will make you feel sexier just knowing you're being so naughty. When the opportunity arises, lean over and whisper that you're not wearing any panties. This gets guys so freaking hot, they practically combust!

THE SET-UP

First, *you* need to meet Betty.

No, she's not a hooker or a horny housewife. "Betty" is a silicone sleeve that has the exact same shape, size and feel of vaginal lips! A few weeks before your trip, order the Best Betty Pleasurizer online at www.ticklekitty.com, or check out other silicone slips at your favorite sex shop.

Before you take off, leave Betty under the sheets in the bed. Tape a note on her that says, *"Hi, I'm Betty. Lube me and use me."*

Game on!

When he is standing at the front door, bummed that your body isn't going to warm the sheets tonight, give him a kiss and tell him not to worry. Betty is going to look in on him this evening! With that, wave goodbye and head out the door.

"Who the hell is Betty?"

Flashing a devilish grin, mysteriously reply, "Well, sweets, I will tell you this—all she's good for is having sex. And you have my permission to have your way with her. Call me as soon as you two meet!"

When you arrive at your destination, give him a quick call: "Hey, honey, have you met Betty yet?" Of course he hasn't—because you hid Betty between the sheets! He'll be bursting with curiosity until he crawls into bed for some shuteye. That's when he'll come face-to-face with this mysterious Betty! Seconds after he reads your note, your phone will ring. "Hey, I just met Betty!"

Ah, the fun begins! Here's your script, Diva: "Good. I want you to lube her up right now and make yourself hard. Then I want you to screw Betty while I'm on the phone with you. I want to hear your moans of pleasure as she wraps herself around your rod."

Talk dirty to him as he plunges inside of her. "Feels just like my pussy, doesn't it? If I was there right now, I would play with myself while I watched you do her." Really get him going as you pull out that vibrator you just happened to pack. "Do you hear that love buzz? I'm playing with myself just imagining you inside her. Mmmm, feels good. Deeper! Deeper!" Don't stop until your man gets you—and Betty!—off.

GODDESS TIP: IF YOU AREN'T SOMEWHERE THAT YOU CAN HAVE PHONE SEX, JUST SKIP THAT PART AND LET YOUR GUY PLAY WITH BETTY ON HIS OWN. UPON YOUR RETURN, CASUALLY ASK HIM HOW BETTY WAS IN BED!

meet Betty...

Every now and then, a Diva has to go out of town, be it for business or pleasure. But one thing is for sure: She would never leave her man all alone!

Time for him to meet Betty....

passion props

Best Betty Pleasurizer

meet Betty...

When the Diva's away, her man
will play...with Betty, that is!

eGG HeaD

He's about to get an eggcellent BJ during breakfast. And his sausage never tasted so good!

THE Set-uP

Set your alarm to go off 30 minutes before your man gets up. You are going to surprise him with breakfast in bed, but breakfast isn't the only thing he is going to be treated to this morning! Head straight to the kitchen and put the coffee on. While the java's brewing, place a muffin on a plate, and then put a raw egg in a bowl. Coffee ready? Pour him a cup and arrange everything on a tray.

Game on!

Gently awaken him and surprise him with his feast. When he asks you if you'll be joining him, whisper that you are in the mood for sausage. *His* sausage, that is! Your lucky man is going to get a nice long BJ this morning, but don't let him come before you get a chance to climb on for a ride. As you pull down his pajama bottoms, school him on the rules of the game:

"I'm going to give you a long, luscious blowjob, but I don't want you to release until I say so. You must hold off until I have had a chance to fully enjoy myself. To insure you do so, I am going to make you hold this raw egg in your mouth while I service you. That way, if you get too excited, there will be more than one explosion in this room! We wouldn't want that to happen!"

Set the tray off to the side and place the fragile egg in his mouth. Stroke, suck, and lick him with abandon. As you lap him up, he will be struggling to keep that egg in one piece. Bring him to the brink of desire before mounting him for some morning love. Make him hold the egg in his mouth a little longer as you grind yourself to orgasm.

Once you've hit your O, it's his turn now. Take the egg out of his mouth and let him pound you until he explodes.

Maybe tomorrow he could serve you breakfast in bed. Pancakes with whipped cream sound awfully yummy, don't they? After all, there are lots of interesting places he could put that whipped cream, don't you think?

GODDeSS TIP: IF YOU are HeSITant to use a raw eGG BeCaUSe OF tHe RISK OF SaLMONeLLa POISONING, SUBSTITUTe a LeMON WeDGe INSTeaD. IF He BITeS DOWN ON IT IN tHe tHroeS OF eCSTaSY, HIS MOUTH WILL Be FLOODeD WITH tart, SOUr LeMON JUICe. PUCKer UP!

eGG HeaD

Morning sex is underrated. After all, you're well rested, you're not stressed out, and you have some time to yourself for a change. Plus, his morning missile is primed and ready to blast off inside you. What a way to start your day!

passion props

Muffin • One Egg
Coffee • Breakfast Tray
One Lemon (optional)

Raise HIS
Temperature!

Long before Florence Nightingale hit the scene, the nurse has been an admired and revered figure for men all over the globe. So why is the idea of a naughty nurse so arousing? Maybe it's because she's a caretaker whose goal is to make his body feel better—*much* better. Plus, she's in control, so the patient must do as he's told if he wants to get special treatment from Nurse Nasty!

THE SET-UP

Tonight, he will be bathing, shaving and indulging his Diva! Tell him to light candles around the tub and draw a shallow bath. After this shaving ritual, you would like him to go down on you and make love to you before you go to sleep. No complaints there!

Have him gather the shaving cream, razor, soap, and washcloth for your mini-spa treatment. Instruct him specifically on what part of your body he will be shaving this evening. Is he only trimming your pubic area, or will he also take care of your underarms and legs? An important part of his training as a good submissive is learning how you like to be served down to the last detail. Be very specific with him so he can do it right!

Game on!

Tell him to lather up the washcloth and clean his Diva from head to toe. Next, he must shave your curlies. When he's doing it right, give him lots of encouragement. Did he nick or scrape your sensitive skin? Tell him he has to kiss it and make it feel better!

Once your bath is over, he is to pat your newly shaved self dry and wrap you in a thick, fluffy robe so you don't catch cold.

Are you satisfied with his performance? Great! Now he's ready for that sex you promised. But you have one more surprise in store....

Instruct him to undress and soak in the same bathwater you did. (Ever heard that line, "She's so fine, I could drink her bathwater"? Don't worry, we're not going to make him go that far!) Just lather him up and bathe your babe. Treat him like he's your property—he must be groomed accordingly. Once he's squeaky clean, we bet he's really ready for that sex....

Not yet!

Say, "Now that you've shaven me, it's time for me to return the favor!" After all, why should he be the only one who doesn't end up with a mouthful of hair after some oral action? (Sounds like a double standard to us....) If he resists, just say those magic words: "It will make your penis look even bigger!" We're sure that's all the encouragement he'll need.

Take the shaving cream and rub it on the shaft up and around the pelvic area. Don't forget his balls! Then shave his jewels very carefully. Take your time. Once he's bare down there, use the shaving cream to stroke and play with him. Pull him out of the bathtub and into the bedroom so you can enjoy some hairless humping. Notice how a good shave subtly changes the sensations you experience when you make love and give or receive oral. Who knows? Maybe shaving each other will become a routine ritual!

RAZOR'S EDGE

Pubic hair is a very personal matter—do you keep yours au naturel (for the retro look), prefer a Brazilian landing strip, or favor something in between? Obviously, these days, less is more, but it can feel like a laborious chore to keep that hair so neat and trimmed all the time. So why not involve your partner in the process? It's highly erotic when he shaves you down there, primarily because it requires so much trust on your part. Plus, when he's more familiar with your puss, the oral sex will be better and longer (since he won't have to cough up a hairball afterward)! A definite bonus!

Passion Props

Candles • Shaving Cream
Razor • Soap • Robe
Washcloth • Fluffy Towel

RAZOR'S EDGE

He's never met a Barber Babe as hot as you! Is he up for some hair care down there?

♪♪♪♪$

naughty nurse

This next procedure might elevate his blood pressure a bit, but that's a chance he's willing to take!

🥿🥿🥿$$

THE Set-UP

Looking the part is key. You can purchase a sexy nurse's costume (made of white cotton or PVC) at a costume store or online. Or, you could always improvise by wearing white panties, bra, garter and stockings. Make sure you have a nurse's cap to complete the look! (If you buy this at a medical supply store, be sure to pick up a hospital gown for him, too, to kick things up a notch!)

Assemble your props on your nightstand, then call your man into the bedroom.

Game on!

Ask your patient to wait there while you go "locate his chart." When you re-enter, order him to completely disrobe. (If you have a hospital gown, make him put it on—otherwise, his birthday suit will suffice.) Tell him to get up on the bed so you can perform his examination.

Get into your role by being completely clinical! Use your stethoscope to check his heartbeat. Make him spread his legs, then poke around his private parts. Then take out your rubber gloves and slowly put them on. This will really psyche him out, as this is what nurses typically do before performing an anal probe. Will it scare or excite him? Hopefully both!

GODDeSS Game 1: WiLD SiDe

Lube your latex gloves, and tell your patient you need to perform one quick little test. Instruct him to lay on his side, then stand directly behind him. Slather a generous amount of lubricant on the inside and outside of his anus. Once his rosebud is lavishly lubed, probe it with your index finger. Slide your digit in and out. But go easy. Ask him, "How does that feel?" or "Does that feel good?" If he says it hurts, slow down. Reach over and give him a hand-job with your other hand. Many guys experience mind-blowing orgasms when they're stimulated genitally and anally simultaneously—so keep this up until he erupts in an ejaculation explosion!

GODDeSS Game 2: MiLD SiDe

Once you have the gloves on, squeeze a fair amount of lube on the palm of your hand then firmly stroke his penis with it. Explain that he needs to achieve an erection for the battery of tests you will be performing. As you stroke him, stay in character by cupping his balls and assuring him that you're just making sure everything is in working order. Once he is fully erect, tell him you'll also need to get a semen sample. But since you're all out of plastic cups, he'll need to ejaculate in your pussy! Pin him down on the bed, then hop on his penis to find out if it's functioning properly. Ride him until you've collected your semen sample—and have experienced a siren-blaring, hospital-quaking O of your own!

nauGHty nURSe

Wow, that sure is a hot patient in room 69. And you've noticed that every time you examine him, he tries to look down your dress or stare at your ass. Well, the next time you check in on him, you might just have to do something about that....

Passion Props

Nurse's Uniform • Latex Gloves
Lube • Stethoscope (optional)
Tongue Depressor (optional)

RUB EACH OTHER THE RIGHT WAY

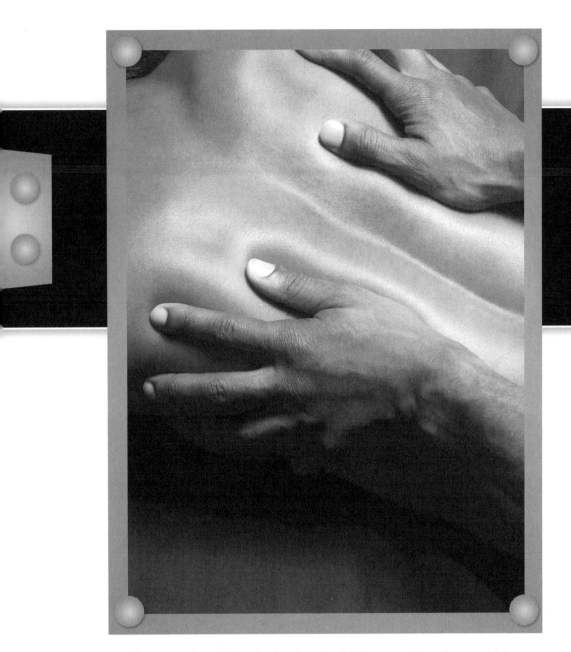

Massages are fantastic foreplay, but there is a definite art to giving a first-rate rubdown. Before applying the oil, rub it between your palms to warm it up. Massage the oil into the top of the neck and gently run your thumbs down the spine toward the lower back. Then, using sweeping strokes, knead the back up to the shoulders. Remember: The skin on the back is thicker, so you can apply more pressure there.

THE SET-UP

Put on your fluffiest white robe (with nothing underneath), and tell your man you're going to treat him to a nice, long rubdown. Instruct him to strip down to his boxers, then tell him to close his eyes and relax: "Visualize the most relaxing place on earth...." Dim the lights, and put on some soothing music in the background to set the right mood.

Game on!

Pour liberal amounts of massage oil on his back and caress him with long, hard strokes. When he is relaxed, ask, "So, is this your first time staying at the resort?" Obviously, he will know he's now staying at a posh resort, and you're his masseuse. Whoa!

Then turn things up a notch by saying, "I noticed your wife is having a massage in the next room. Are you on your honeymoon?" Now it's clear that his wife is being rubbed down next door. What a mental image that paints!

Next, lean down and let your breasts rub against his back. "Think your wife will mind if I rub you like this?"

The thought makes him hot. Then: "Why don't you roll over so I can give you a full-body massage?" Even hotter. When he rolls over (at full attention, no doubt), don't be shy with the oil. Rub him nice and slow at first. Then faster. And faster. The first time he moans (and he will), whisper, "Shh! Your wife will hear!"

Undo your robe so he can catch a glimpse of your beautiful body. Encourage him to touch it. Whisper, "Do my breasts feel better than your wife's?" You bet!

While he feels every glorious inch of you, begin to moan. Then say, "Oops...I should be quiet or else your wife will hear how well you're rubbing me down there!"

As he reacts, seductively whisper, "Or maybe she should come in here and lick me while I'm sucking you off!"

Aah...just the mere thought is enough to send you both over the edge, isn't it? The role-play can go many places from there—maybe you pretend his wife does come in, or you continue to try to silence your sensual screams—but it always ends in the same place: Orgasm City, the hottest, most exciting place on Earth!

sex spa

If you tried "Massage Parlor," you already know that massage role-play is unbelievably erotic. The oil…the rubbing…the pure pleasure—how can you go wrong? Some games are just so hot, they inspire a repeat performance…with some tantalizing tweaks, of course!

Passion Props

Robe • Soothing Music
Massage Oil

sex spa

He's enjoying an erotic rubdown while his "wife" is just in the next room. Can he silence his moans of desire?

👠👠$

catch a
BUZZ

You're trying your hardest to make your guy climax while he's trying his hardest not to come. In this game, winner takes all!

⌁⌁⌁$

THE SET-UP

As you're getting ready for bed tonight, take charge. Tell him that you are going to take his clothes off and play with him. If he tries to help you undress him, push his hands away and sternly tell him no. He's your toy, and you can do whatever you want with him! Push him onto the bed as if you are going to mount him. Tie both his arms above his head with the first scarf. Next, secure his ankles together with the other two scarves. Now you have him right where you want him!

Game on!

Spend a few minutes stroking and kissing your property. At this point, he'll be sure he's about to get some hot sex. But tell him that all depends on whether or not he can be a good boy and stop himself from coming too soon. In fact, he can't come until you say so.

It's called cock training, and school is now in session!

Slowly strip off your clothes in front of him, teasing and tantalizing him. Now, take out your trusty vibrator and pleasure yourself with it for a few minutes. Make him watch! Then straddle him on the bed and place the vibrator between your crotch and his. Both of you will feel the buzz! Applying this sort of pressure will also make it more difficult for him to control himself. Remind him that if he even thinks about releasing in your presence, you are prepared to discipline him! (What's his punishment? You decide!) If he starts to get close, turn off the vibe and remind him to follow your orders.

Wait a few minutes for him to calm down, then sexually torture him again—only this time, do it even longer. For example, if he was able to withstand 20 seconds of the vibe last time, kick that up to 30 seconds now. Slowly count down as he struggles to hold his impending orgasm at bay!

If you are feeling truly sadistic, tell him it's obvious that he's not concentrating hard enough. Therefore, you have no choice but to start the countdown over—vibrator still in place!

Repeat this exercise until you think he's about to blow, and then give him permission to release. Demand that he looks you in the eyes as he climaxes so that he remembers exactly who he is coming for: you!

Once his shuddering has subsided, untie him and tell him it's payback time. He needs to sexually compensate you for all that cock training you so kindly gave him. Force him to use that vibe on you until you explode in ecstasy!

CATCH A
BUZZ

Ever since they were invented way back in 1869, vibrators have been beloved by Divas everywhere. But who says your guy can't get in on the fun? Before bed tonight, you'll play nice and share your favorite sex toy with him. But not before laying down some Diva ground rules designed to make this game a little more interesting....

PASSION PROPS

Three Scarves
Vibrator

TAKE YOUR
BEST SHOT

According to a recent survey, 42% of men say they enjoy being spanked while having sex. And no wonder: When you spank him during foreplay, it can enhance arousal and make sexual feelings more intense. A spank or squeeze generates body heat by bringing blood to the skin's surface and releases oxytocin in your system—which increases testosterone production, thereby increasing sex drive. Plus, it's a mental turn-on, too: Suddenly, he's the bad boy who's in big trouble. You'd better teach him his lesson....

THE SET-UP

You're the sexy babysitter, so make sure you look the part. A white blouse, tight skirt, sexy panties, and stockings with garters scream, "I'm in charge!"

Game on!

Start the scene in the doorway where all this sneaky spying has been going on. Lightly grab "Tommy" by the ear, lead him to a corner of the bedroom, and order him to stand there and stare straight down at the floor. Now that you know his dirty little secret, he will be punished for peeking in on you! Tell him that you know that he watched you put your silk panties, garters, and stockings on this morning. (Describing the outfit that you are wearing will put his mind right where you want it…in the gutter!) Order him to turn around so that he can see that sexy attire he's been sneaking peeks at all week.

At this point, you have no choice but to spank him. If he is going to act like a bad boy, he will be treated like a bad boy—bottom line! Sit down on the bed and beckon him over. Pull his pants and underwear down around his ankles. Caress his genitals to get him erect for the beginning of the spankfest.

Bend him right over your knee so that he is close to you and can feel your skirt and stockings on his groin. Aim for the middle part of his butt, and spank him lightly at first with a slightly cupped hand. Tell Tommy how naughty he's been for peeking at you. Alternate between fondling his genitals and delivering the next swat. He's been such a sneaky pervert! Spank him just hard enough to create a rosy hue on his cheeks. Be sure to rub his bottom between spanks to ease the sting.

Once you've spanked him for a few minutes, it's time for him to assume another position. Make him lie facedown on the mattress while you administer his "corporal punishment." Take your time. Tell him to grind the bed as you spank him. Whisper dirty things in his ear after each blow. Make him beg for the next swat!

When his butt is red (but before his balls are blue!), tell him you want to spank him while he's inside you. Make him get on top so you have easy access to his butt, and spank him each time he enters you. Don't stop until you've both exploded in ecstasy!

GODDESS TIP: RAKING HIS BUTT LIGHTLY WITH YOUR FINGERNAILS AFTER A FEW SMACKS WILL GIVE HIM A REAL RUSH!

SPY WHO SHAGS ME

You are staying with "Tommy" (a.k.a. your man) while his parents are away on vacation. You have just noticed a peephole in the guest bedroom and realize that he has been watching you get dressed every morning! And probably touching himself, too....

Needless to say, Tommy's in BIG trouble now! And you're gonna make him pay!

Passion Props

White Blouse • Tight Skirt
Sexy Panties
Stockings with Garters

SPY WHO SHAGS me

He's been a very naughty boy. It's time to bend him over your knee for a well-deserved spanking!

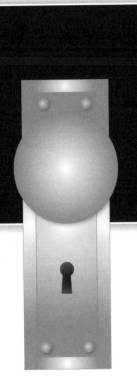

ABDUCTION
SEDUCTION

Your guy better watch his back tonight. Someone's about to take him against his will....

⌐⌐⌐⌐$$[

THE SeT-UP

You will need to do some pre-play prep the day before this game. First, make reservations at the hotel of your choice—either swanky or seedy. Then pack an overnight bag for yourself and your man, making sure to include all the passion props.

E-mail your man at work on Game Day. Your message should look something like this:

Hey Babe,

Surprise—I've made reservations for us at _____ tonight . Meet me there at 7 p.m. sharp. I'll call your cell at 6 p.m. to give you the room number. When you get there, please be careful. I have heard that there have been a lot of abductions in that area recently and I wouldn't want to lose you!

Love,
Your Diva

Arrive at the hotel early to check in and set the stage. Change into something very dominant, such as a black corset with garter, stockings, and heels. Your costume should convey that you and you alone are in charge tonight! As 7 p.m. approaches, grab the blindfold and scarves or ropes, and wait by the door.

Game on!

When your man knocks, stand behind the door as you open it so that he cannot see you. As he walks in, order him to stand still while you secure his hands tightly behind his back. Place a blindfold over his eyes so he can't see his surroundings. The hand restraints and blindfold will make him feel like he's being taken prisoner—and that's exactly how you want him to feel! Strip him from the waist down and tie his ankles together with the rope or scarf. Lead him to the foot of the bed, and then order him to sit down and wait for further instructions.

Tell him you're taking him prisoner and holding him for ransom. He must comply with your every demand in order to survive! Rip your hostage's blindfold off so that he can soak in your beauty and ponder his predicament. If he does not get completely hard by looking at your sexy ensemble, then tell him that you are disappointed that his prick isn't perfect enough for you. As you rub his rod, ask how he likes being held against his will. Stroke him to erection perfection.

Now release his hands from behind his back and reposition them over his head so that you can have your wicked way with him! Crawl on top of your "victim" and tell him you want to test the merchandise. Go ahead—mount him. He might not get out of this room alive, so he should try to enjoy his last screw! As you ride your captive closer and closer to orgasm, remind him that if he comes before you do, he will definitely not live to see tomorrow! Then bounce up and down on your passion prisoner and let the sexual sparks fly....

abduction seduction

Hotel sex totally rocks. But this is hotel sex like neither one of you has ever experienced before. You'll feel like you're caught in your very own action movie...which is fitting, since you'll definitely be getting some "action" before this night is through!

Passion Props

Hotel Reservation • Stockings
Heels • Two Ropes or Scarves
Blindfold • Garter • Bra

BE FEARLESS
IN THE BEDROOM

To truly become a Dominant Diva, you've got to push your sexual boundaries and stray out of your comfort zone. We hope these games will help you do just that—and serve as a springboard for intense, no-holds-barred sex each and every time you hook up. Before you know it, you'll be transformed into a try-anything lover who's no longer on erotic autopilot. Kick ass!

THE SET-UP

Before you begin this evening's activities, you are going to buy (or borrow) a few wigs. If you're a redhead, for instance, you'll need a brunette and a blonde wig. It's best to buy at least one wig that's the opposite of your normal hair. If you have short hair, purchase a long, flowing wig. Already have long locks? Try a cropped wig for a totally new look—and feel. Put that one on first for maximum impact.

Early on in the evening, hide the wigs and a silk blindfold under your pillow. Then once you go to bed, pounce on your man. (Be sure to leave a light on, though—he needs to see you to fully appreciate what's going to happen next.) Give him a long, deep, passionate kiss that leaves no doubt he's getting lucky tonight. Then pull out a silk blindfold from under your pillow and tell him he's in for a hair-raising surprise. Secure the blindfold in place, and whisper that your friend Janine is coming over...and that you hope he likes blondes. He won't know what to expect. Are you bringing another girl over? Huh?

Game On!

Put on your wig, then kiss him again. Let the foreign locks rub along his chest. Once he realizes that's not your hair, he'll be even more excited. Slowly take off his blindfold and let him take you in. You're beautiful. But you're not...you. Not tonight, anyway. You're his fantasy girl.

Slowly kiss down his belly and stick your hand in his boxers. Ask him if he's ever gotten a BJ from a blonde before. Now make it happen, but don't let him come. Ask him if you give a better BJ than his wife or girlfriend. Then give him a kiss goodbye and put on his blindfold again. Time for the next wig. Tell him you're going to send your roommate Cindy over. You hope he likes brunettes....

Put on your wig and get ready for round two. It's best if the second wig feels a lot different from the first. If you went with a cropped one the first time, use a long one now. Let the locks rub against his body. Wrap the hair around his manhood, and rub it up and down. Tell him that Janine told you he was good in bed, and you've come to see for yourself.

Now, take his blindfold off. Let him take in every inch of the beautiful brunette you. Command him to lick you down there. Tell him you're going to tell his girlfriend/wife how well he follows orders. Threaten to call "her" if he doesn't do it right. Once he's licked you to satisfaction (but before you hit your O), sit on his lap once again and put his blindfold back on. Tell him you're sending his wife/girlfriend back home, and he'd better confess all he's done tonight.

Get up and take off the wig. Open and shut the door for effect. Then stomp over to him, and rip off his blindfold. Give him a nice, long kiss, and tell him you heard he's been naughty tonight. And you love it. Tell him that even though the other girls got to be with him, *you're* the only one who can truly push him over the edge. Then prove yourself right!

WIGGED OUT

Tonight, your guy is going to have

sex with three different women...

A blonde.

A brunette.

And a redhead.

Does the carpet match the drapes?
Not exactly. But he won't notice.
He'll be too dizzy with desire.

Passion Props

Two to Three Wigs
Silk Blindfold

WIGGED
OUT

Does your man fantasize about being with more than one woman at once? Tonight, you're going to make that happen—but don't worry: You'll be the only Goddess in the room!

◢◢◢$$

YOU
Bet-cha!

When you took a gamble on love, you definitely hit the jackpot. But now, the stakes are higher than they've ever been. Will winner take all? It's in the cards!

THE SET-UP

First, select your game of choice. Poker? Pool? Bowling? Miniature golf? Any activity is fine, as long as your skills are as evenly matched as possible. This will keep the competition fair.

Game on!

Once you've decided on a sport, it's time to create your carnal cards. You must each write down five sexual fantasies you'd like the other person to fulfill. Focus on positions or sex acts that you've always dreamed about. Maybe he's longing for you to go down on him while you play with his balls. Or perhaps you're jonesing for him to do you doggie style while fingering your clit. Write down one dirty desire per card and then fold it over so your partner can't peek. Place the cards in your bowl. The loser of each round will be forced to draw one carnal card from the winner's bowl and perform the act described on it.

Let the games begin! Play to win here. If you're competing in a public place, such as a miniature golf course, you can either select your cards right there on the course (hot!), or wait until you get home. Either way, your round will be sexually charged. *Fore!*-play, anyone?

Playing at home? You can always perform the sex acts as you go (like after each hand of poker, for instance), or just hold off until the end so you can have one big lovefest. You make the call!

If either one of you selects a carnal card that is just out of the question, remember: You have final veto power. You don't have to do anything you don't want to do. This is supposed to be fun for all parties involved!

So, play to win. But don't worry: If you lose the first round, there's always round two. We see multiple orgasms in your future!

GODDESS TIP: IF POKER IS YOUR PLEASURE, WHY NOT PLAY STRIP POKER TO MAKE THE COMPETITION EVEN MORE INTERESTING?

YOU
Bet-cha!

A little friendly competition between lovers can be a very good
thing, especially when you have
some high sexual stakes riding on
the game! Now when he calls you
a "player," it will take on a whole
new meaning....

Beat him, Diva!

Passion Props

Index Cards
Two Pens • Two Bowls

OFF THE HOOK!

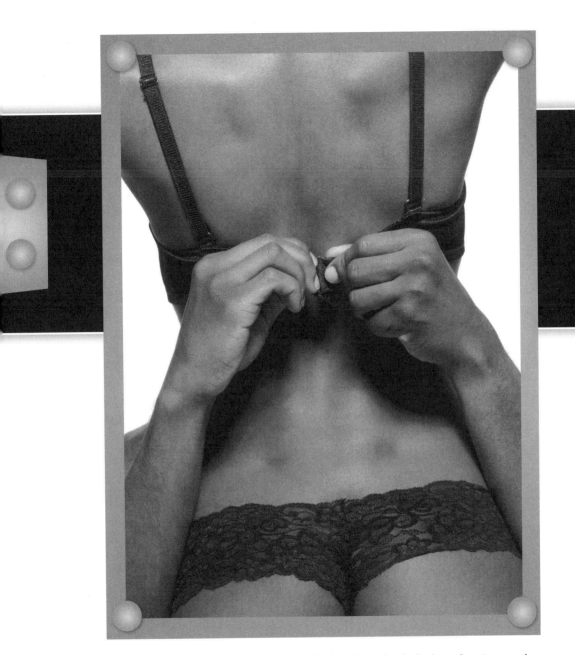

Unfastening your bra takes him straight back to high school. In those days, it seemed like it would take a rocket scientist to figure out how to do it. How he'd wished there were written instructions back then! But every millisecond he wrestled with those hard-to-control hooks, he only got more and more turned on. He couldn't wait to see those magnificent mammaries! So instead of just tossing your bra aside in the heat of passion, ask your man to take it off for you. He'll be yours hook, line, and sinker!

THE SET-UP

Today, you are going to be home to greet her when she walks in the door after a long day at the office. If your Diva works from home or watches the kids during the day, you are still going to lighten her load at 6 p.m. sharp. Take that purse, briefcase, or load of laundry from her hands and replace it with her drink of choice. As you lead her to a comfy seat, ask her how her day was and really listen to what she has to say. While she settles in, take her shoes off and give her feet a nice little rubdown before putting her slippers on. Allow her to unwind as you start dinner or order in. If you have kids, occupy them and tell them not to disturb Mom. Your goal is to completely pamper your Diva!

After a nice quiet dinner (and when the kids are sound asleep), refill her drink while you draw your sweetie a warm bath. Light candles while you tell her that you plan to cater to her every need. (Every Diva's fantasy!) Take her clothes off and help her into the warm water. Bathe her every inch, lavishing extra attention on all her moan zones. Next, lather and rinse her hair, then gently massage her scalp. Not only do scalp massages feel amazing, they will release pleasure-inducing hormones into her bloodstream that will boost her pleasure!

Game on!

By now she is completely relaxed—well, almost. If you have a shower hose, flood her privates with the warm jet stream. Many women masturbate this way, and it will be a special treat for you to do it for her. Don't have a hose? Just turn the water faucet back on, making sure the temperature is just right—nice and warm, but not *too* warm! Tell your Diva to close her eyes, spread her legs and place her clitoris directly under the faucet. While she enjoys the water-works, tell her how beautiful she is and how much you love her. Kneel down and kiss her neck and ears. What a feeling!

Once she hits her O, tell her to soak for a few more minutes while you do one more thing. Take her fluffiest towel and favorite pajamas and place them in the dryer for five minutes. That way, when she slips out of her luxurious bath, they'll be nice and toasty warm for her. Heaven!

Dry her off slowly and lovingly. Blow out the candles and drain the bath while she slips into her pajamas. Next, walk her into the bedroom and tuck her in for the night, telling her how much you adore her and that she means everything to you.

Now it's time for you to get ready for bed. If your Diva is fast asleep by the time you join her, then you executed this scenario perfectly! She's no doubt having sweet dreams of you and only you. Well done.

Bed Bath
and way Beyond

"Honey, I'm home!" How many times have you watched a dated television show that begins with the housewife greeting her husband at the door, immediately taking his briefcase and handing him a stiff drink? Households just don't run that way anymore, unless they're firmly stuck in the 1950s. (How retro!) But maybe those television icons were onto something. Pampering your Diva after a long day is the perfect way to show her that you love and adore her, and it really doesn't take much planning.

Passion Props

One Cocktail • Slippers
Fluffy Towel • Pajamas • Candles
One Dinner (Homemade
or Take-Out)

BED BATH
and way Beyond

men's
ROOM

Water is so erotic—and tonight
you're going to explore all its passionate possibilities. Let's just say
you've never gotten her wet quite
like this....

PLUG It In

men's ROOM

You've had some wild, kinky sex in the past, but this will kick your lust up about 10 notches. Guaranteed to shock and amaze....

♪♪♪♪$

THE SET-UP

A few days before the game, try toying with your Diva's butt while she's on top during sex. Is she receptive to your finger play? Ask her if she'd like you to do her with a butt plug. If she's into it, check out plugs online or browse for one at your local sex shop together. Plugs come in many shapes and sizes, so she should pick out the one she'd feel most comfortable with.

GAME ON!

Your Diva knows that she will be trying out her new toy at some point, but she doesn't realize that you have a hot role-play planned tonight that will enhance the experience. First, turn her on with a little foreplay action. Rub her down, lick her up, and steam her seam. Once she's dripping with desire, flip her over and prep her for the anal invasion. Be sure to use lots and lots of lube beforehand.

Lie face up on the bed and command she straddle your stiffy. Now blindfold her as she bounces up and down your hard rod.

Take the plug and gently insert it in her anus. As you enter her, whisper, "Can you feel me filling up your pussy? How about my friend who's taking you up the ass? We're both going to do you tonight!"

Once she's moaning and groaning, slowly begin to move the plug in and out, in and out. Really screw her with it. The feeling of your pounding penis inside her, combined with the back-and-forth gyrations of the butt plug, will definitely make her feel like she's having sex with two guys at once.

Talk dirty: "I know that you're always fantasizing about two men taking you at once, so I asked my buddy to come over and give you a test drive. You love it when we fill up both those holes, don't you?"

The two-on-one sensation will send her head spinning!

Make sure she experiences an out-of-this-world orgasm before you allow your own rocket to blast inside her. Who knows? This scene is so hot that she just might have three or four orgasms before the night is through!

FUTURE VARIATION: MAKE HER SUCK YOUR INDEX FINGER WHILE YOU ARE DOING HER BOTH WAYS. THEN TELL HER HOW MUCH YOU LOVE WATCHING HER SUCK ANOTHER GUY OFF WHILE A THIRD GUY DOES HER UP THE BUTT. SUDDENLY YOUR DIVA'S GOT THREE GUYS IN HER BED INSTEAD OF JUST TWO! WHOA!

PLUG It In

Play a little mind game with your Diva between the sheets! Wouldn't it be ballsy to make her feel like she's in the middle of a hot three-some this evening? Of course, you would never want to share your cherished mate, but a small butt plug and a little role-play can go a long way!

Passion Props

Butt Plug

LOVE YOUR LUST LIFE

When you have an amazing sex life, it affects all aspects of your relationship in a positive way. There's less fighting. More communicating. Less stress. More connection. We believe that playing sex games with your man will boost your bond big time!

THE SET-UP

Before he leaves for his trip, slip a note in his suitcase that looks something like this:

I hope you had a safe trip, Doll. I miss your hot bod already—but even though you're not here, I still have a sexy surprise in store! You will receive a call tonight promptly at 10 p.m. When the phone rings, you will be asked to accept the call. Do so and listen to the very special recording that I have chosen just for you. This message will verbalize all the naughty things that I want to do to you, but I thought it would be fun for you to hear them from another woman. You don't know her—don't worry. Just think of her as Madame X!

Pleasure yourself while you listen to her. But think about me while you do it! If you haven't come by the end of the message, you can listen to it again until you do. Don't stop until she's pushed you over the edge.

GAME ON!

There are tons of recorded sex calls you can order for him on the Internet. Our favorite is www.niteflirt.com, where you can choose from a wide variety of genres: straight sex, girl-on-girl, domination…you name it, they have it! They're cheap, too. The average recording runs six minutes at approximately $1.99 a minute, so 20 bucks goes a long way.

It's titillating to choose the recording you're going to send your lucky man. Read summaries, check out ratings from other users, and browse photos of the phone sex operators. You can even test the recording out by sending it to yourself first just to make sure it will turn him on. (Be sure to order a recording that's at least five minutes long so he has enough time to get off!) Once you decide on a listing and enter your credit card information, you'll be asked to type in your man's cell phone number and then the call will go through right away. If he is expecting the call at 10 p.m., you must be on the computer at that same time to order the greeting. Familiarize yourself with the site ahead of time so you'll know how it works.

There are countless websites that offer similar sexy services. Check out our website at www.dominantdiva.com for an updated list of our favorites.

Of course, nothing can seduce your man quite like your sultry voice. Tomorrow night, provide a live encore!

GODDESS TIP: EVEN IF HE'S NOT OUT OF TOWN, YOU CAN STILL GIVE YOUR MAN THIS SEXY SURPRISE. SEND HIM A PHONE SEX MESSAGE WHEN HE'S IN THE NEXT ROOM!

on THE
ROaD aGain

It's always fun to play sex games with your man when he goes on the road for business. Even though he's not with you physically, you can still manipulate his love muscle from across the miles....

passion props

Phone Sex Recording

ON THE
ROAD AGAIN

He's about to get an emergency call
on the road. And the emergency is
that he's about to feel very horny!

Take me to the Drive-in

Steam up those windows! If the car

is a'rockin', don't come a'knockin'.

THE SET-UP

Before you head out to the drive-in, don't forget to bring along a large bag of popcorn and a blanket. After all, the two of you are on a hot date tonight!

Game on!

Once you park, hop in the backseat for some make-out madness. Spread the blanket over both of your legs to give yourself easy "undercover" access. Then explain the rules of the game. You are going to play with, tease, and sexually torture your man. Whatever you can do (without the other moviegoers catching you in the act) is fair game!

At a drive-in, you can get away with a lot! Start by giving him a prolonged hand-job—one of those slow and deliberate strokefests that he's probably bragged to his buddies about.

His mission? He cannot let on that there is anything going on between the two of you! (It's poker-face time!) He must succeed in his mission or the two of you just might get thrown out. How embarrassing! You certainly don't want that....

Do everything in your power to divert his attention from the screen. Rub him down. Amp him up. Make him hot!

If you happen to be in a regular cineplex, you will have your work cut out for you, as discretion is of the utmost importance. Try going to an off-hours showing for a more private theater experience. But remember: The goal here is not to cause a scene or bring attention to yourselves. You need to keep your desire on the down-low.

Do you think you can push him over the finish line? We dare you!

But why should he have all of the fun? Once he's gotten his rocks off, direct his hand under the blanket for a little action of your own. Forget watching the movie. Instead, concentrate solely on the sensations you're experiencing as he diddles you to a strong, two-thumbs-up orgasm.

Take me to the Drive-in

Believe it or not, drive-ins are still around! It may take a little research to locate one of these retro relics, but they do still exist. If you absolutely cannot find a drive-in anywhere nearby, the regular ol' cineplex (or, in this case, *sin*-eplex) will work, too. Select a seductive movie or romantic comedy to set the mood. It's showtime!

Passion Props

Popcorn • Large Blanket
Movie Tickets

THE FRUITS
OF HIS LABOR...

Ready for some fruity fun in the bedroom? Make him feed you grapes while you make love. Dip pear slices in warm fudge and have him rub them all over your body—then lick you clean! Place a mango slice in your puss and encourage him to take a bite. Licking the sticky nectar off his Diva's hot, salty skin is enough push all of his bliss buttons!

THE SET-UP

Prepare an afternoon picnic for just the two of you. This feast can be served anywhere, as long as the locale provides complete solitude. If you have a backyard, that's probably your best bet.

Dressing the part is important as always, so put on that pretty sundress. No panties, please!

Ask your guy to pack the goodies: wine, glasses, sandwiches, and chips. While he's doing that, you can pack the passion picnic basket. This will include whipped cream, strawberries, and two scarves. Pack your basket on the sly, as you don't want him to see what you have in store. Don't forget the blanket and CD player!

Game on!

Find that secret picnic spot and set everything up. Have a nice lunch and enjoy each other's company. Don't rush a thing! Enjoy the sunlight, listen to the music, and pour another glass of wine. This is what weekends are all about! Sometimes we cram so much into a weekend, we forget to devote time to each other and ourselves. Today, you're making up for that lost time.

At some point during lunch, he'll probably ask what you have stashed in the other basket. Just tell him to save room for dessert, and then give him that devilish grin that he knows all too well!

Take out the blindfold from the passion picnic basket and tell him you have something special planned. Cover his eyes with the scarf. Tell him to lie down on the blanket, and start feeding him strawberries. Lick the juices off his lips. Slowly take his shirt off and unzip his shorts. Wouldn't his penis taste good with a little whipped cream? Give it a go! Once you've had your fill, hike up that sundress and spray the whipped cream on your love lips so he can have a taste, too.

Once he's licked and teased you, tell him you're going to place a scarf over your eyes as well. Mount him. That way, you'll both be blindfolded while you bonk! Not being able to see will heighten all your other senses. Suddenly, the breeze will feel cooler, the grass will feel softer, and his moans will sound louder.

Play with each other. Use your fingers and mouth to explore all those unseen body parts. Enjoy the feeling of exhibitionism as you roll around on the blanket. Remember: You can't spell "outdoors" without "O"—so go ahead and hit yours!

carnal connoisseur

It's Saturday morning and you and your man are enjoying a hot cup of java and reading the paper. Sounds like the start of a typical weekend, doesn't it? Well, your morning might be ordinary, but your afternoon will be anything but. The best part of this sexual adventure? It takes place in the great outdoors!

Passion Props

Wine • Glasses • Sandwiches
Chips • Whipped Cream
Strawberries • Two Scarves
Blanket • CD Player
Picnic Basket • Two Blindfolds

carnal connoisseur

When's the last time you went on a romantic picnic together? You're long overdue for a rendezvous.

CHORES 'n more

Today, you're going to turn your working man into a *hard*-working man in every sense of the word!

♪♪♪$$

THE Set-UP

Start by asking him to reserve two hours on Saturday to help you with some chores around the house. That morning, change into a '50s style housedress. You're the woman of the house today—and you need to look the part.

Game On!

Once Saturday comes, make your guy change into his uniform: a flannel, pair of jeans, and a tool belt. Yum! Then hand him a short list of chores:

- Sweep the garage
- Change all lightbulbs
- Check the pipes

Playfully tell him that if he doesn't do his chores properly, you will be forced to bend him over your knee for not doing as he is told. That should catch his interest!

Explain that you'd like him to get turned on while doing chores for you. To help with that, show him the remote-controlled vibe or cock ring you've purchased, and then attach it to his penis. But, no matter how much you buzz him, he's not allowed to release during his chores under any circumstances, or else he'll really get a spanking!

Now, sit back, relax, and read a magazine while he does all his hard work. This is the way it should be! Turn the remote-controlled vibrator on and watch him wiggle and squirm while he's working. Bring him to the edge as he's sweating over his manly chores!

If he's moving more slowly than you would like him to, give him a few swats on the ass for poor performance. That will kick him into gear!

Once he's done his work to your satisfaction, tell him he needs to complete one last task before taking that tool belt off. He must get on his knees, crawl up under that housedress and pleasure you. While he is finishing his final "chore," remember that you still have the remote control in your hand...so use it.

GODDESS TIP: Remote-controlled vibrators or cock rings are so popular these days and are an absolute must for your sexual bag of tricks! They generally run about $50 and can be purchased at most adult boutiques. If you prefer to shop online, visit our site at www.dominantdiva.com for an updated shopping directory.

CHOReS 'n more

It takes time and effort to be a Diva, so you definitely need a break now and then.

Ready for him to pick up that broom and sweep you away?

Believe it or not, many men fantasize about doing manly chores for their Diva. Georgia's clients love running errands and doing things for her! So today, you're going to put your guy to work and make all his dreams come true.

Passion Props

Remote-Controlled Vibe
or Cock Ring • Flannel Shirt
Jeans • Tool Belt

SHOW HIM
tHe ROPeS

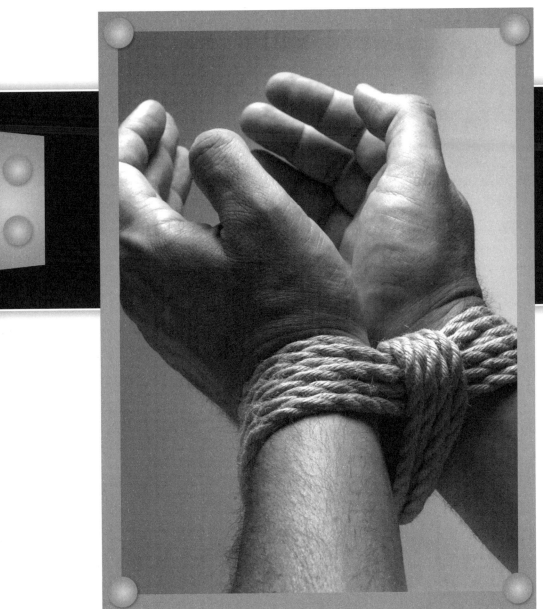

Wanna lasso your lover? If you're not a former Girl Scout, freak not: You can still easily learn the "ropes" of rope. Using rope with a thicker band (vs. thinner rope) will make the restraints more comfortable for your partner. Never tie the rope too tightly, or you could cut off circulation to his hands (which means he couldn't rub you with them later)! To avoid rope burns, use soft cotton rope instead of the stiff, coarse variety.

THE SET-UP

Your boudoir must be primed and ready by the time he gets home. (Hint: To give yourself plenty of time, tell him to arrive at 7 p.m. sharp—no sooner, no later!) Make sure the room is clean, as laundry on the floor or an unmade bed can seriously squash a sexy vibe. Place lit candles in strategic places around the room, then place a blindfold, long rope, and handcuffs on the mattress.

Dress the part. After all this build-up, wearing sweats and a T-shirt would be a major letdown for him—and you! If you dress sexy, you'll feel and act sexy, so it's worth it to make a little effort here. But you don't have to go crazy: A matching panty and bra set would look hot, but doesn't require much fuss. (Bonus!) If you want to go the extra mile, a garter and fishnets would push him off the charts. Black or red are both colors of dominance, so sticking with those is key.

At 6:55 p.m., unlock the front door, then hide in a locked bathroom until you hear him come in and follow your orders. If you answer the door, this will ruin his surprise.

Game on!

Once he's waiting for you in the bedroom, it's time for you to have some fun! When you enter the room, walk around him slowly and tell him to look up at you. When his eyes meet yours, say in your most seductive voice, "This is the last time you're going to get to see me. You had better soak every inch of me in before I blindfold you!" Explain that you are going to stuff your soaked silk panties in his mouth if he dares to utter a single word. After you slowly and seductively blindfold him, roughly grab his hands and hold them in front of his crotch. Place the handcuffs on him, and tie the rope around the chain that connects the two cuffs. Put his arms straight up, and have him bend his elbows toward you. Then put his hands behind his head, so that the rope falls behind him past his butt. Whisper in his ear that the two of you are going to play a game called Stand and Deliver, and his job is to just *stand* there while you *deliver* the best BJ of his life! Tell him he is not allowed to release until you allow him to, and that if he does, he will be punished. Get down on your knees and play with his penis. At the same time, hold the rope tightly between his legs, which will secure his hands behind his head. His penis is now your *property*.... Stroke it, tease it, and really try your hardest to get your slave to disobey your orders. Every now and then, pull on the rope to remind him who is really in charge. Make this game last as long as possible by repeatedly taking him to the brink, then pulling him back. Make him beg! When you feel that he can't take it anymore, give him permission to climax. Ah, sweet release....

Once the earth stops quaking, tell him that for being such a good boy, he now gets to pleasure you as his reward. Time to lay back and enjoy, Diva. You deserve it!

stand and DELIVER

This racy sex game begins right before he goes to work. Tell your man to expect a call from you while he is at the office. At some point during the day, leave him a voice mail saying that when he gets home, he must go directly into the bedroom and strip down completely. Then command that he stand at attention, eyes cast downward, to await further instructions. Slam down the phone and let him stew all day over the deliciously naughty things you are going to do to him!

PASSION PROPS

Candles • Blindfold
Long Rope • Handcuffs

STAND AND DELIVER

The 9-to-5 grind can be a real pressure cooker. That's why guys love turning over the power reins to their Diva after hours....

THE
COLLAR

Who's in for some red-hot oral
action? Let's hear a collar holler!

◢◢◢◢$

THe set-up

Create a written invitation that reads:

One night this week, you will serve my every need and desire. Check the bedroom doorknob immediately after work for the next seven days. When you see a collar, put it on and wait inside the bedroom on your knees for further instructions.

(If you have kids, ask him to check under his pillow before bed every night instead.)

After you give him the invitation, wait a few days before breaking out the collar. Give him some time to obsess over what you are going to do to him. Men love a little mystery, and you've just given him loads of it, Diva!

The night of the big "reveal," put on a black slip and garters with stockings before placing the collar on display.

Game on!

Once he discovers the collar, give him enough time to put it on and drop to his knees like a good little boy. Then enter the room. Lightly grab his hair and pull his head backwards. Look into his eyes and give him a deep, long kiss. Tell him to put his hands behind his back while you undress him.

Once he's naked except for the collar, it's time for him to service his Diva! Command him to lick you while you're standing up. If he isn't satisfying you properly, tell him what you'd like him to do next or any improvements you'd like him to make. Higher, lower, faster, slower!

When he's licked you long enough, tell him to lie face up on the bed. Handcuff his hands above his head, then lick and tease his rod during your fellatio fest.

Tell him that he must not release, and that if he comes close before you are ready, you will stop and leave him in the handcuffs all night. Bring him to the brink a few times, and then stop. Grab his collar. Tell him you just don't think he's ready to come yet (even if he's completely ready to burst).

The next time he comes really close to orgasm, punish him by getting up to fetch a glass of water. By leaving the room, you'll only extend his ecstasy.

Once you return, give in to temptation and make love to him. Tell him he can only release once you have counted down from 20. Keep gyrating and grinding him until 3...2...1...blastoff!

THE COLLAR

This is a game that takes a lot of confidence. You're completely in charge of what happens tonight… and he will do exactly as you say. Be firm. Be authoritative. He'll only be allowed to come when you say so. The more brazen you are, the bigger the orgasms will be for both of you. Be a Diva!

PASSION PROPS

Collar • Handcuffs • Black Slip
Garters • Stocking • Heels

REACH OUT AND TOUCH SOMEONE

Having phone sex is way hot—but a lot of people are just too embarrassed to actually do it. If you feel freaked out about getting busy via Ma Bell, follow these pointers. First, start off by lowering your voice an octave. You'll sound and feel sexier. Then describe what you want him to do to you, along with what you'd like to do to him. Ask him questions that move the action along: How would you like me to touch you? Harder, softer, faster, rougher? Go with the flow. Before long, you'll feel like an old pro!

THE SET-UP

Check out your local paper or erotic websites for a steamy 1-900 number to dial. Or go to our website (www.dominantdiva.com) for an updated list of numbers that have earned our seal of approval. Many phone sex services offer a variety of specialties from straight phone sex to domination—so go ahead, pick your pleasure! Calls generally cost anywhere from $1 to $10 per minute, which can most definitely add up. To control costs, put an egg timer next to the phone and set it for the total number of minutes you can afford.

A speakerphone adds a whole new dimension this scenario—but if you have kids or room-mates, set the volume low enough so the whole house doesn't hear your steamy phone sex!

Once you've chosen your number, put on a hot bra and panty set, and fetch your man. Lead him into the bedroom and command him to strip. Then tell him to get on his knees while you sit on the bed, phone in hand.

Game On!

While your man is waiting patiently for further instructions, let him in on your naughty little game. Tell him that within moments, the two of you are going to call another woman—a smoking hot woman, at that. If you've got a picture of the phone sex operator, show it to him and say, "This sex goddess is going to decide what you do to me tonight. You are to follow all of her instructions. Do you understand?" Your guy's head will be reeling with excitement and anticipation. This is every man's fantasy...and, tonight, you are going to reap all the rewards!

Okay, time to set your timer, then smile and dial. Let the operator know what's going on immediately—after all, the clock is ticking (literally)! Say, "I have my love slave here, and for the next 10 minutes, he's going to do to me whatever you require or desire." Tell her he needs lessons in pleasing you. If you want him to do something in particular, tell her that he hasn't been licking you enough lately, or that he just won't try new positions anymore. When you drop specific hints like that, she'll be more likely to put him in his place!

Now put him on the phone so she can tell him exactly what to do to you—and how to do it. For the next 10 minutes, lay back and enjoy all the pleasures she commands. Leave it to another Goddess to help you get all the worshipping you deserve....

Once your call is complete, make your man finish you off (if he hasn't already)! By then, he'll be ready to combust—and will be practically begging for you to give him some Diva love! Tell him he's been a good love slave...so, as his reward, he gets to have you for 10 minutes. Set the timer again—just knowing he has to beat the clock will turn him on even more. While you're making love, ask how he liked taking orders from another woman. Just hearing you talk about it will be enough to send him straight over the edge!

1-900
sex me

The thought of having a ménage a trois: Hot. The reality of having a ménage a trois: Not ever gonna happen, for most. But tonight you'll get to experience the thrill of having someone else in the bedroom without actually going through with it. (Everybody wins!)

Passion Props

1-900 Number
Egg Timer • Phone

1-900
sex me

Remember that old saying, "Two's company, but three's a crowd"? Well, it's time to put that theory to the test.

How's this for a magic trick? Have hotel sex without stepping foot outside your home!

THE SET-UP

First, pull a Nancy Drew and find out the hotel where he'll be staying. Do this immediately after you hear of his trip, as you will need time to mail a package to the hotel in care of his name. If you only get a few days' notice, shell out a few extra bucks to mail it overnight. Contact the hotel in advance to find out any requirements they have for guests receiving packages—you want to make sure this gets to him. The package will contain the following:

A collar • A pair of your panties carrying the scent of your perfume (or your natural musk!) A small bottle of lube • A red envelope carrying explicit instructions

The outside of the red envelope should say something like this:

Enclosed are directions for a little sex game I have planned for you. I would like for you to wait to open this until 11 p.m. (or right before bed). Then follow the instructions inside.

The naughty note inside should read:

Did you think your penis wouldn't have any fun just because you're out of my reach? No way! As you can see, I have provided a few select toys for you to use for my pleasure.

First, I would like you to place the collar around your neck in honor of your Diva. The lube will be used for you to prepare yourself. I want your penis in high salute when you call. I am waiting by the phone to continue this game across the miles. Oh, and make sure my sweet, sniffable panties are handy as well. Call me now!

Game on!

When you hear the phone ring, make sure that you are camped in the privacy of your bedroom, where you can speak freely. Ask your man if he liked his special delivery and whether or not he has done as you asked. Go down the list with him. "Is your collar on? Are my panties handy? Is your rod at full attention thanks to the lube?" Tell him you'd like him to touch himself and make that dick even harder.

Describe all of the sexual things you'd like to do to him! This is the time to get really graphic. Dirty words and deeds are a must when it comes to phone sex. Is he nice and hot? Better yet, are *you* nice and hot? Good! Drive him to the brink of orgasm, but make him promise not to release until you say so. Tell him that you want him to listen to you hit your O first!

Turn on your handy vibrator or finger your clit while you describe exactly what you're doing to yourself! Let him know what he is missing. Moan how much you wish he were there to touch you, lick you, do you! Once you explode, it's his turn. Tell him to sniff your panties while he makes himself come! That should do it....

Both of you should now be way satisfied even though you aren't even sharing a bed tonight. Sweet dreams, Diva!

FeD XXX

The next time he's going away for business (or pleasure) without you, don't despair. In a way, you'll be coming along on this trip, too. No, you're not going to hide in his suit-case—but you are going to sneak into his thoughts in a sexy way!

The coolest thing about this game is that it shows you have made the extra effort—and that's such a turn-on for your partner! He'll feel like the luckiest guy in the world....

passion props

Collar • Bottle of Lube
Panties Carrying Your Scent
Packing Box • Red Envelope

earn some
extra credit

Playing out taboo fantasies such as schoolgirl/teacher doesn't mean you're both total pervs. As long as you're consenting adults and the fantasy remains just that—a fantasy, there's no harm in pretending that he's your hunky math teacher from senior year while you get it on. After all, some of your first crushes were likely on teachers—and some of his were probably on the schoolgirls who sat next to him in class. This way, you both get to tap into those long-forgotten feelings buried deep inside.

THE SET-UP

Assemble your passion props on the nightstand beforehand. Ask your Diva to put on a sundress or something that the "girl next door" might wear. Then tell her to meet you in the bedroom. Place a chair in the middle of the room, and ask her to take a seat.

Game on!

Lock her hands behind her back with handcuffs or scarves. Secure a blindfold tightly around her eyes so that she cannot see. Sometimes the best way to heighten her senses is to take one away!

Once she is secured to the chair with the blindfold in place, tell her why she's there. She might look and dress innocently, but everyone in the neighborhood knows what kind of a slut she is! So you've got guys lined up outside her door to get a little piece of the action.

Let her hear you unzip your pants and pull your dick out. Tell her that the neighbor from across the street is standing in front of her stroking himself. The neighbor is actually you, but you are of course playing the roles of all the men tonight! Since she can't see what's going on, you'll send her on quite a head trip by describing the different guys who are coming and going—or, in this case, coming and *coming*.

Get your member nice and hard by rubbing it right in her face. Whisper that you watch her all of the time in her tight little sweaters, and that you can't wait for her to wrap her lips around your big hard dick. While she is servicing you, tell her how slutty she is and that her conservative clothes don't fool anyone. Close your eyes and savor the sensations of her tongue on your flesh. But no matter how turned on you are, don't let her suck you off just yet. It's the next neighbor's turn!

Leave the room for a moment, allowing her to anticipate the next guy's arrival. Put on some unfamiliar cologne to intensify that feeling that she's with a total stranger!

When you re-enter the room, don't talk much at all. This "neighbor" is quiet and rough. Force your thing deep in her mouth and just mutter for her to "suck it hard." This time, she does such a good job that you explode in her face! Then, without a word, leave the room.

She is left to contemplate her predicament as the third neighbor walks in. You've really got her going as you take a look at her wet face. "Hmmm, seems to be all used up. Maybe I'll just take a little taste of honey." Go down on her. Between licks and slurps, tell her that you're going to take her down the street when you are done to let the frat house have a crack at her. The best way to really get into her mind is to get graphic, so talk dirty. Tell her she's a little slut. She's not that innocent! And you're going to make sure that she spreads her legs all over the neighborhood. Rock her c-spot by fingering and licking her until she reaches ecstasy.

GiRL next DOOR Gone BaD

Playing a role that's different from their own personalities arouses many women. One of those roles is the girl next door gone bad! Tonight, you are going to play game master and weave a web of sexual pleasure around your Diva.

The light bondage and blindfold used in this sex game will take all responsibility away from her and allow her the freedom to really get into the head space that you have created. Just tell her to trust you, and then take your Diva where no good girl's ever gone before.

Passion Props

Handcuffs • Scarves
Blindfold • Chair
Cologne

GiRL next DOOR GOne BaD

men's ROOM

It's time for a neighborhood block
party like no other. Guess what?
Your Diva's the main attraction.

⏶⏶⏶⏶$$

aFteR-SCHOOL
SPECIAL

When she's sent to the principal's

office, she's in deep trouble. Do

the crime and do the time!

◢◢◢$

THE SET-UP

Today you are going to dress her up in a cute little tight white blouse, miniskirt and bobby socks with heels! Costume shops (either local or online) offer a wide variety of schoolgirl uniforms ranging from innocent to erotic. Of course, there is nothing wrong with raiding her closet! She probably already has a fitted blouse and miniskirt. Just add pigtails, and you're good to go. (But under no circumstances is she allowed to wear panties!)

Start the scene in your home office. You are the principal, and she's the schoolgirl who's been called in for bad behavior. Maybe she got caught smoking in the bathroom or skipped detention. Now, she has been sent to your office to be punished.

Game on!

Tell your schoolgirl to knock on the door. When you let her in, make her sit down and ask her if she knows why she has been sent to the office. If she doesn't answer right away, remind her of why she's in trouble. She doesn't want you to call her parents, does she? Of course not...and she'll do whatever it takes to make sure you don't make that call!

Invite her to sit on your lap. Tell her you are going to have to teach her a lesson. While you contemplate her punishment, slip your fingers under her skirt. She isn't wearing any panties! What a bad girl walking around school all day with nothing underneath. No doubt she teased all the boys as she breezed up the stairs to class. Now, you are really going to teach her a lesson. No more Mister Nice Guy!

You have a ruler on your desk, and it's time to use it. Make her bend over the desk or table, then hike up her skirt. Quite a vision, but you have a job to do! Spank her several times with the ruler and make her apologize for her bad behavior. Go easy, as the ruler is not as forgiving as you might be. Just smack her booty hard enough to capture her undivided attention.

But she's such a bad girl, the ruler isn't enough to correct her behavior. She needs something more. Immediately force her to her knees and pull out your throbbing manhood. Maybe she should keep her mouth shut so that she doesn't get herself in any more trouble. But first, she needs to open wide so you can give her a little taste of what her principal's packing!

She looks hot as hell, but don't come yet. Not until you bend that naughty schoolgirl over your desk and take her from behind, anyway....

This is one lesson she'll never forget!

after-school
special

There's something so sexy about seeing a grown woman wearing a school uniform. Maybe that's why there are about a zillion pornos out there with this same storyline. Who needs a porno when you can live out your fantasy for real? Your Diva is going to get an important lesson from the principal today.

Passion Props

Schoolgirl Uniform
Ruler

SHOW him some tough LOVe

You already know the physical benefits of rough play (like that endorphin rush he gets when you smack him on the ass), but playing rough is a mental mind-tease, too: Your sexual aggression communicates your desire to him, which turns him on even more. You want him and you want him now—and nothing's going to stop you! Rough play is also hot because it's so passionate. This shows him that you're wild, uninhibited and way into his body—a tantric trifecta.

THE SET-UP

Let your man know before work that today is game day and he should be expecting you to contact him at some point. Call him during work hours to let him know that he has an appointment with you in your home office immediately after work. Tell him that he didn't meet his sales quota, and that the two of you are going to have to come to some sort of an agreement in order for him to keep his position. Give him a time to be there, and warn him not to be late.

Before he gets home, break out that smart and sexy business suit and some killer pumps. If you have glasses, wear those, too—or even consider investing in some non-prescription ones. Put your hair up to complete your severe but sexy look.

Game on!

When he knocks on the office door, stand up and tell him to come in. There is nothing more intimidating than a gorgeous in-charge woman towering behind a big desk! Tell him that you're sure that he knows why he is there and that you are very disappointed with his performance lately. You simply feel that you have no choice other than to let him go. Unless...he agrees to your unusual, yet effective, method of correcting his poor attitude in order to keep his job! Order him to drop his pants so you can see what he has to offer. Any protests will get him fired. If he has a hard-on, point out that if he can't even control himself in the presence of a beautiful woman, how could he possibly control his clients?

You plan to teach him how to cater to customers today by servicing you. After all, sales is a service industry. But first, he must be punished for not living up to company standards. Your methods may seem unorthodox, but you know what you're doing, and you don't want him to question you or undermine your authority. Since his pants are already down around his ankles, that leaves a bare ass just waiting to be whipped. Tell him that you are going to treat him as if he were in grade school again and spank him. Take your panties off and stuff them in his mouth so that the other employees won't hear his yelps. Then proceed to give him a sound spanking!

After you get his ass nice and warm, remind him that he needs to learn a thing or two about pleasing people. Take the panty gag out of his mouth, and then order him to his knees. Saunter back to your desk. Tell him that since you are so successful, you rarely have time for your own pleasure. From now on, he is to come straight to your office and pleasure you before he attends to his daily duties. He'll meet your every need, and right now you need him to lick your puss. If his services are not up to par, he will get another spanking—only this time, it will be with his own belt. But if he services you well, he might just score a promotion...to having sex with you, too!

Once he licks you and completes his task, it's time for more training. Make him watch as you hike up your business suit and bend over the desk. Tell him to screw you hard! He'd better get you off or he will be demoted. Have fun, Boss Lady! Who says it's lonely at the top?

BOSS Lady

Men just love to fantasize about women in the most obvious power position: The Boss Lady. She's that she-devil bitch who's the secret object of their desire. This power-house wears tight, revealing suits to drive the guys wild. And her sexy high heels are perfect for stomping peons on her way to the top!

Is this what most Boss Ladies are really like? Of course not. But it's his fantasy, and he's sticking to it. So, use that to your advantage, Diva, and become the Boss Lady of his dreams. He's going to give you whatever you want...or else!

Passion Props

Business Suit • Pumps
Eyeglasses

BOSS LADY

You're a real slave driver at the office...and he's about to find out for himself just how demanding you can be.

Beck 'n Call

He's meeting you for a mystery meal. "Let's do lunch"…then do each other!

THE SeT-UP

Ask your man to keep three lunch dates free for you this week. What days are best for him? Once he gives you his schedule, let him know that he must be available to do whatever you want during those long lunch hours—but you'll only be available one day. Which one? Don't tell him just yet. The name of this game is anticipation. Tell him if he gets a call from you at 11 a.m., that means you're on for lunch. Otherwise, he's released from his "on-call" duties.

On each of the three days, put on something really special in the morning (like those diamond earrings you usually save for special occasions, or that dress that drives him wild). This will psyche him out and make him wonder if "today's the day!" You can bet that you will control his every thought until lunchtime! Also, place an empty picnic basket in his trunk, but don't let him know it's there.

Game on!

On the chosen day, call him at 11 a.m. and tell him that there is a picnic basket in the trunk of his car. He has 45 minutes to purchase everything on the list of items that you are about to fax over to him. He must place them all inside the picnic basket, and then bring it to you.

It will excite him to know that he is actually going to get a fax from you. Will the fax overstep his personal boundaries? What will it say? He will just have to trust you. The fax should look something like this:

I look forward to our lunch meeting today. Please pick up a turkey sandwich on wheat bread, a small bag of pretzels, and two Diet Cokes. Oh yes, and a can of dog food. See you soon!

If anyone in his office sees the fax, they won't think anything of it, as it looks just like a grocery list. But don't make the fax blatant in any way! The idea is to play with his head and get those wheels spinning before he arrives. Of course, he will think that the dog food is for him (especially if you don't own a dog), but it's really just there to psyche him out. Also, notice the fax didn't list any lunch for him! That is because you have already bought his lunch...but he doesn't know that!

Hopefully, he will complete his task and be there on time. If he is even five minutes late, tell him he'll get five spankings later. He needs to learn not to keep his Diva waiting. Once he arrives, make sure that he completed his task to your satisfaction, then enjoy your lunch (minus the dog food, of course). Surprise him with his favorite foods so he can join you as well!

Bon appetit! If you are able to sneak in some uninterrupted alone time, there is no time like the present to get a little love! You both planned a long lunch, so why not make the most of it?

Beck 'n Call

Don't you just love going to lunch with your man? It's great to break up your day by seeing your sweetie. This week, you're going to ask him to devote three lunch hours to you and only you. The catch? You'll only meet him one out of three days. (During the others, he'll just have to fantasize about you!) A Diva always keeps her man on his toes and leaves him wanting more!

passion props

Picnic Basket • Fax Machine
His Favorite Foods

some say that
LOVE IS BLIND...

When your man is blindfolded, his other senses are heightened…making him all the more acutely aware of the sweet smell of your perfume, the taste of your skin, and the sound of your husky voice in his ear. Because he can't see what you're doing to him, his level of anticipation will skyrocket. And when his sight has been stolen away, his mind will fill in all the visual blanks—which can be sizzling hot for both of you.

For this game, it is crucial to dress the part. This will take a little planning—but, believe us, your payoff will be more than worth it.

Think dominatrix. When dressing like a domme, you can't go wrong with leather, rubber, or lace. (And high heels complete any outfit, so don't forget your stilettos!) Form-fitting catsuits are hot, hot, hot—and skin-tight corsets positively scream "worship me," the main message you're sending tonight. While the most elaborate get-ups can cost upward of $500, you can also score a PVC or vinyl dress for under 50 bucks. Whatever you spend, you will definitely get your money's worth out of these fashions—tonight and any night thereafter. For inspiration, stop by your local lingerie store or check out our website at www.dominantdiva.com for an updated shopping directory.

Once you've chosen an amazing ensemble, leave this note in his briefcase (or anywhere that he is bound to find it):

Dear Love Slave,

Meet me at 7 p.m. in the bedroom tonight. You will take off all of your clothes and wait for me on your knees with your eyes cast downward. You will only look at me once I give you permission. Come prepared to please.

Mistress Diva

Remember to get home an hour before he does and set the stage. Put on some sexy music, light candles around the room, and lay the following toys on the bed: a studded collar, one long shoelace, a silk scarf, and a crop. Thirty minutes before he is to arrive, get ready in another room. Make sure you lock the door, and that you're well out of sight. He is not allowed to see his gorgeous, dressed-up Mistress Diva beforehand, as this would ruin his sexy surprise.

When the clock strikes 7, it's showtime. If your man has followed your instructions like a good boy, he'll be on your bedroom floor with his eyes cast downward. Make a grand entrance, making sure your stilettos click, clack, click along the floor. Lean down and let him smell your perfume. Let the fabric of your costume rub against his neck. Remember—he still isn't allowed to see you, so awakening his other senses will make his pulse race!

If he tries to sneak a peek (and he probably will), order him to look at the floor. He must earn the right to gaze at a Goddess like you—and he just doesn't deserve to yet! As you place the collar snugly around his neck, tell him that it represents the fact that he is your slave and that he should always know his place. Tell him that he must always have his hands placed behind his back unless you give him permission otherwise. This is a sign of true submission. Place a kiss on his lips. If he tries to kiss you back, warn him again that he is not allowed to do anything without permission—he is only there to serve. Let him know that when he misbehaves, his privileges will be taken away. Tie a silk scarf around his mouth so that he remembers the rules. Lightly kiss him through the scarf so that he can see what he is missing. Hmmm, he is so close, yet so far....

THE SESSION
PART ONE

Welcome to The Session. All of the sex games in this book are "sessions" of sorts, but every daring game has been leading up to this grand finale. Tonight, you'll transform into the ultimate Dominant Diva, and your man will be your love slave. There's no doubt you're up to the challenge.

PASSION PROPS

Sexy Music • Scarves • Collar
Candles • Dominant Outfit
Shoelace • Crop (optional)

THE session
PARt one

Everything you've done up to now
has prepared you for this final mission. We know you're ready!

♪♪♪♪$$$

THE SESSION
PART TWO

Tonight, he's visiting a world-class dominatrix. Her name? Mistress Diva, of course!

⚘⚘⚘⚘$$$

Tell him to stand. You would like to see your prized penis in high salute. Be sure to tell him his penis is *your* penis. After all, his entire body is your property—and that includes everything below the belt! Take the crop (or your fingertips) and bat your prize around a little bit. You don't want to hurt him—just swat him around enough to get him fully erect. Guys love this. You're stimulating him in all the right places while making him feel like an object at the same time. When he's at full attention, allow him—finally!—to gaze at your perfect body. This look he has awaited so long will likely take his breath away. Tonight, you are a sexual superhero, and he's about to experience your superpowers!

After you make him tell you how beautiful and amazing you look, it's go time. Spank him, crop him, play with his prize, and tease him. See if he can take five or 10 swats on his butt in order to receive a reward. If he pleases you, he may be released from the scarf and be allowed to kiss your beautiful booty. What a worthy slave he is, getting to kiss the Mistress's ass.... If he takes even more punishment, you might just decide to let him make love to you, but only if he pleases you first.

Turn him around and tell him that he has to bend over and touch his toes. He is going to take what you dish out in order to earn a piece of your luscious love cookie. Give him 10 more swats on his behind. Tell him that for each swat you would like for him to say, "Thank you, Mistress." Rubbing his rear after a few swats will ensure he'll be able to take the next few. (Again, the spankings aren't meant to hurt too much. You just want to give his cheeks a nice, rosy hue.) If he survives his entire punishment, it's time for his second reward. Take the shoelace and tie it nice and snug around the base of his penis and balls. Make sure that this is a looooooong shoelace so that you can use the ends of it as a leash. If you have to tie two shoelaces together to get this effect, do it. That way, you will really have your love slave by the balls, literally! Tell him that he's been such a good slave, he is now going to be allowed to take you from behind. Even though this is traditionally more submissive for the woman, keeping the "leash" on his penis the whole time puts you in the position of authority. If you want him to do you harder, just tug on the leash and tell him to work, dammit! Every now and then, make him slow down and worship your booty just to remind him who's boss.

Don't let him release until he's sent you over the edge once (or, better, twice). When you're done with your play toy—but not a second sooner!—he can finally have his just desserts. After all, his slave labor is no longer necessary.

Well done, Mistress! You are now officially a Dominant Diva in every sense of the word. Celebrate your fabulousness—because you rule. Viva la Diva!

THE SESSION PART TWO

You're doing a really amazing job, Mistress Diva! Being in control is the power trip of a lifetime…and the night's only going to get better and better. Prepare to experience the wonder of his worship!

PASSION PROPS

One Dominant Diva Attitude
(You go, Diva!)

congratulations!

You have brazenly busted each and every Door of Desire open and experienced the orgasmic thrills of all 69 sex games with your partner. That means you know firsthand exactly...

HOW to Be a Dominant Diva!

Think back on all the great sex you've had over the past few months. There's no doubt you've transformed into a wildly inventive lover who is always willing to take chances between the sheets. You're sexually free, fearless, and fabulous!

So what now? First, log on to our website at www.dominantdiva.com to read even more sexy scenarios and meet other Diva graduates who are just as amazing as you. In the coming days, months, and years, use this book as a springboard to continue your sexual adventures. Revisit some of your favorite games. Hell, make some up of your own!

Be Daring. Be Dangerous. Be a Dominant Diva!